Where There's a Will

JUNE FRANCIS

FRANCIS

Where There's

a Will

1⊡ CANELO

First published in the United Kingdom in 2020 by Canelo

Canelo Digital Publishing Limited
31 Helen Road
Oxford OX2 0DF
United Kingdom

A CIP catalogue record for this book is available from the British Library.

Print ISBN 978 1 80032 008 6
Ebook ISBN 978 1 78863 711 4

Look for more great books at www.canelo.co

Printed and bound in Great Britain by Clays Ltd, Elcograf S.p.A.

Chapter One

Mildred Martin looked down into the byre at the sow and her squealing piglets. They looked so adorable as they wriggled and squirmed against each other to reach their mother's teat, and she thought what a nice simple life they had, wishing she could say the same for her own; she then remembered that the piglets would grow up to have their own problems she supposed, at least she wouldn't end up on someone's dinner table.

Giving a sigh, Milly wrinkled her dainty nose, tipping half of the large bucket of scraps she was carrying into the feeding trough and watched as the sow roused herself to feed, scattering the piglets as she shuffled towards the food. As she straightened up, she flicked back a reddish-brown plait.

Feeding the livestock wasn't the worst thing about life on the O'Donnell family farm in County Cork but it was one of them. It seemed to Milly like a hundred years ago since she had lived in Liverpool with people around her that she could call friends. She thought wistfully too of her Liverpool granny, Adelaide Martin. It had been five years since she and her mother had lived with her paternal grandmother and that was the last time her life could be described as even half normal. Even then it had been spoilt by the constant squabbles between her mother Bridget and her grandmother, especially since the news had come from Ireland that her father, Joseph, was missing presumed dead as a result of the Irish Civil War. Yet still they squabbled. Grandmother Martin blaming her daughter-in-law for persuading Joseph to live in Ireland after their marriage instead of near his own family in Liverpool.

Milly's father had been a sailor and while he was at sea, Bridget had missed her family in Ireland, and had returned there, taking little Milly with her. Once back from his voyage, Joseph had followed them to Ireland and that was how he had become involved in the Irish Civil War.

Her memories of what her daddy looked like were vague, but she had a warm feeling when she thought of him and missed him very much, though she did remember he used to put her to bed and tell her stories and call her his 'darling daughter'. She had never forgotten how his fair-coloured beard tickled when he kissed her goodnight or how strong he was when he swung her up in the air when he came in from working in Great-grandad O'Donnell's cabbage and potato fields or helping to milk the cows or feed the pigs, like she was doing now.

Then had come the day when her daddy had insisted that his wife and daughter return to Liverpool without him to stay with his mother at her home near Stanley Park. He had hugged and kissed Milly and waved goodbye as the ferry left the Port of Cork and she had never seen him again.

Fortunately, Milly liked Liverpool and her grandmother's house had been much grander than she had been used to in Ireland. There were dainty teacups and saucers laid out on frilly doilies which her grandmother used for afternoon tea and each dinnertime there would be meat served on plates with cutlery, unlike at the O'Donnell farm where they ate Irish stew out of clay bowls most days except on Sundays.

Granny Martin had insisted on Milly attending the local school and Milly soon settled down and made friends. At first her grandmother and Bridget rubbed along alright, concealing their differences as best they could, but after a time tempers frayed and complaints about the other's behaviour were let fly. Milly hated them arguing and would slip out and hurry to the kitchen where Susan, the housekeeper and Dot, the tweenie, always made her welcome. Susan taught her how to make jam tarts and gingerbread men and when her mother and grandmother were both out, Dot taught her how to play two balls against the house wall, as well as hide and seek in the house which was very large with an attic on the top floor and a cellar for the coal down below.

Milly had sobbed on her grandmother's shoulder when word had come of her father's disappearance after an explosion. Milly didn't understand what had happened exactly, but he was reported as missing presumed dead and her grandmother had been frozen-faced and tight-lipped as Bridget read the letter from home imparting the news.

Eventually their differences would get the better of her mother and Adelaide and the two women would go at each other hammer and tongs. One night during a bad row carrying on downstairs, Milly had sought to shut out the shouting by pulling the bedcovers over her head until she heard footsteps outside her door.

Her mother opened it and entered, 'I know you're awake, Milly,' she said. 'Get up and get dressed!'

Milly did not move until her mother approached the single bed, dragging the bedcovers from her daughter's hands and saying sharply, 'Do as you're told! We're getting out of here. I've had enough of that old hag.'

'But it's dark, Mammy, where will we go?'

'We'll find somewhere, don't you worry,' Bridget said.

'Are we going to Ireland to find Daddy?'

'No, Milly, just get your things and we'll be away.'

After that their lives had taken many a twist and turn in the intervening years. They did return to Ireland eventually, but had never found Milly's daddy and now here they were, come full circle back in County Cork. The house was full of four generations of O'Donnell's, including her great-grandfather, her grandmother, as well as Bridget's uncles who tended the family farm.

Milly walked back through the yard still carrying the half-full pail of scraps and was about to head back towards the cottage when she caught sight of her great-uncle Willie approaching from the house. Recoiling in horror, she wondered what had brought him back from a visit to Cork earlier than expected.

There was a name for men like him that she had learnt from the mothers in Liverpool who would have called him a 'dirty old man', the kind who hid up back jiggers and who young girls were warned to avoid.

Shuddering, Milly wished her daddy was here, still able to remember the feel of his moustache tickling her cheek as she wound her young arms around his strong neck when he carried her up to bed to tell her a story and tuck her in.

Willie's shoes crunching across the cobbled muddy farmyard brought Milly's thoughts back to the present and a fearful trepidation caused a chill to travel down her spine. She wished now she had accompanied the rest of the family to church after all. It was a couple of miles away and she had neither wanted to be squashed into a pony and trap which made her feel sick, or to walk in the mud and rain, so despite the disapproving tuts of the family, she had chosen instead to stay back and do her chores — feeding the pigs and preparing the vegetables for dinner. Milly believed herself safe as Willie had told them he'd gone to play cards with some friends in Cork last evening and had not been expected home until later that day.

–

When her mother Bridget had explained they were going back to live in Ireland with her family, the O'Donnell's, Milly could recall little of the farm she had last seen when she was a small child.

Their journey on the boat from Holyhead to the Port of Cork was a choppy and unsettled one. They had been collected by her mother's uncle, Willie, in a horse and cart and Milly saw very few of the smart motor cars that had become a feature of life in England as they journeyed slowly through country lanes.

Once they arrived, Milly disliked the way the family bombarded them both with questions about their lives in Liverpool. Though Bridget had sworn her to secrecy about the things that transpired there, their curiosity hinted that they knew there was more to Bridget's story than she was letting on.

Milly told them to mind their own business when they pressed her and they told her she had no manners which set the tone. When her grandmother O'Donnell asked Bridget about Milly's schooling and church attendance, she made a big show of being shocked to learn that Milly had gone with her granny Martin to the Protestant church and school. Her Irish grandmother wasted no time taking Milly with the rest of the family to the nearest Catholic church. Milly found the Mass service far too long and boring; the heady incense and the Latin incantations made her feel drowsy and a little sick so now she avoided going altogether which was another reason for the family to badger and berate her.

Despite Milly being in her teens, the O'Donnell family believed in children being firmly down the pecking order. There seemed to be no suggestion of any more schooling for Milly and she had been expected to take up her jobs on the farm just like the rest of the family.

She had enjoyed the fresh air and learning about the livestock, but as time passed it always seemed to be raining, and it was a constant battle to keep clothes, shoes and her thick woollen socks dry. Getting up at five o'clock in the morning to light the grate and set the water to boil in the kettle felt like drudgery. The men kept to their jobs in the fields and the woman took care of the house and all the tasks involved.

It was worse for the men out in all weathers, Milly could see that, but all the same, some days it was awful for her too. There were few children her age, save the ones at church but they just looked at her like she had arrived from Timbuctoo; she couldn't bear the way they stared at her. Milly knew her mother hated it too; however, it was not Bridget who was up at dawn but Milly with her mother grumbling beside her, insisting Milly get up to light the fire.

Uncle Willie used this to his advantage often catching her on her own. At first, he had made it seem like he was her friend, taking her out in the gig and showing her the fine city of Cork, helping her out with her chores and sharing snippets of news from his paper. Uncle Willie was middle-aged, but still considered himself handsome with a good head of curling fair hair mixed with slight touches of pepper. Milly's widowed grandmother thought the sun shone out of him and Milly could not understand why Willie was not married.

The first Christmas came and went, and Milly was starting to realise Willie's breezy manner was just for show; he was idle, never doing a hand's turn out in the fields, unlike his two bachelor brothers, Patrick and Callum, and his father. Occasionally, the other two daughters of the house who had married came to stay. As the eldest son, Milly also noticed that Willie held his mother in the palm of his hand and she wouldn't hear a word said against him.

Willie had then started to make sure he and Milly were alone together and things had taken a darker turn. He would sidle up to her when she was out in the stable or peeling vegetables in the kitchen and would speak to her in a way she considered over-familiar.

Milly knew about the things that men and women did together which her Granny Martin would have called the 'birds and the bees', but what Willie did to her was wrong and he knew it too.

Then the day came when he put his arm around her shoulder and fondled her breast inside her blouse. She froze, shocked and frightened out of her wits. Then anger stirred inside her and she tore herself free. 'If you do that again I'll tell Grandma,' she said breathlessly.

'She won't believe you,' he jeered. 'She had no time for your English daddy and she doesn't approve of you either. Thinks you have too much to say for yourself with your English ways.'

Milly's heart sunk, that was likely to be true, but then she straightened her backbone. 'I'll tell Great-granddaddy.'

Willie shrugged. 'I bet you don't. It takes guts to talk of such things and you'll only shock him by mentioning it – and it's not as if your mammy pleased him by marrying an Englishman out of the faith. We're all glad he's dead.'

Tears welled in her eyes. 'If he was here, he would knock your block off for daring to lay a hand on me. Anyway, he's only missing.'

'You believe what you like but I reckon he's dead. If he's alive, he ran away because he's something to hide.' He took several paces towards her and thrust his face into hers before she could back away.

'If you say anything the scandal would kill your grandmother and you and your mammy would have to leave and be forced on the streets.' He sneered at her.

'We have friends in Liverpool, they'd help us.' Milly retorted.

'They aren't here now though, are they?' She knew he was right.

–

These days Milly tried her hardest to avoid Willie, but she didn't always succeed, sometimes he would catch her on the stairs, or he would engineer things so that he caught her upstairs while she was making the beds. She felt like she was living on her wits and thanked God that at least she and her mother shared a bed because goodness knew what he would do if she had her own bedroom.

Milly was convinced the family would never believe her if she told them of his disgusting behaviour when he caught her alone. Now, as he approached her with that sly look on his face, Milly's knees began to quake, and she was convinced she was about to faint and into her head came thoughts of what he could do to her while the rest of the family were at Mass.

'Keep away from me, you filthy, lecherous old man.' Milly tried to stop her voice from shaking as he got closer.

'Now, now, that's no way to speak to your elders and betters.' His tone was mocking.

'Betters!' Milly was angry now. 'You're no better than those pigs in the sty, in fact they are head and shoulders above you.'

'Come on Milly.' He took a step towards her. 'Let's kiss and make up.'

Milly held the pail full of old cabbage tops, potato peelings and used tea leaves in front of her like a shield. 'One step closer and I'll tip these right over your old rotten head.'

At this, Willie took a step back, probably thinking Milly thought, of his best suit that he was still wearing from his night out. 'You wouldn't dare.'

'I certainly would, you wouldn't look quite so fancy covered in pig's swill!' She shook the pail at him in warning.

'Why you little—' Willie made to lurch toward her but at that moment they both heard the clatter of the cart and the clop-clop of the horse's hooves as the family drove up the path back from church.

'I won't let you touch me again,' Milly hissed at him. 'This is the last time you'll come anywhere near me, do you hear?'

'We'll see about that.' Willie said and then turned on his heel back towards the farmhouse.

Chapter Two

Once inside the house, Willie disappeared upstairs, while the family who had been to church removed their coats and muddy boots in the hallway.

Milly had come through the back entrance into the warm kitchen, the air was chilly now that autumn had arrived, and found her mother there already.

'Why is the dinner not on? What have you been doing since we left for church?' Bridget eyed the vegetables still waiting to be peeled and boiled.

'I've the lamb joint in, it won't take long to get them ready.' Milly placed the pail by the back door, ready for the peelings and thought it was a good thing she'd been carrying it when Willie had approached her.

'You're awful flushed.' Her mother scrutinised Milly's features with a frown. 'And you've a guilty look on your face.'

'What do you mean? I've done nothing wrong.' Milly was indignant.

'Well make sure you get on quickly now, your uncles will be complaining if they have to wait much longer for their meal.'

'If it's so important, why don't you roll up your sleeves for once and muck in.' Milly's eyes flashed in anger.

'You cheeky slut, I don't know what has got into you today.'

Milly couldn't hold in her feelings any longer. 'Why did you have to bring us here, all it ever does is rain and I'm nothing better than a drudge here. I've no friends and worse than that…' Milly hesitated.

'Come on spit it out,' Bridget snapped.

It was now or never, Milly thought. 'Uncle Willie has been… taking liberties.'

Her mother's eyes narrowed. 'What are you talking about, what sort of liberties?'

Milly's mouth felt like it was full of cotton wool, but she was determined to speak up. 'When he gets me alone he touches me in places he shouldn't. And it's getting worse, he won't stop unless someone steps in.'

Shock and then anger registered on her mother's face. 'You're making it up. You just want to go back to Liverpool.'

'That's not true, I'm not a liar and you know that.' Milly's lips started to tremble, her mother had her faults, but she had to believe her.

'I know nothing of the sort, only that you'd do anything to get away from here, it doesn't suit you and you've had enough of housework.'

'That's all true and I've made no secret of it. Sure, we are only here because you're running away from your own lies. Why don't you tell them the truth if it means so much to you?' Milly couldn't help herself but the words were out before she could stop them. 'You have a son that isn't Daddy's and you have to keep it a secret otherwise Grandma O'Donnell will throw you out!'

'You just keep your mouth shut,' Bridget hissed at her daughter, throwing a look over her shoulder to make sure none of the family were in earshot. 'If they find out about Charlie, we'll both be out on our ear.'

'I don't care any more, life can't be worse than this.'

'Opening that can of worms will cause more harm than good.'

Milly and her mother eyed each other. The secrets and the tensions of the last few years festering in the air between them.

Uncle Willie chose that moment to enter the kitchen. 'Well now, how about a little sit on my knee, Milly?' He said this before realising that Bridget was in the room too.

He stopped short and pulled nervously at his tie. 'Sure, that was just a little joke, Bridget. We like a little laugh don't we Milly?'

Milly felt sick, but looked to her mother. 'Mammy?'

Her mother paused for a minute, appearing to weigh things up, then said, 'Get on with your peeling Mildred and I'll lay the table. Willie you can tell me the gossip at your card game last night.' With that she ushered him out of the kitchen, not before shooting a look her daughter's way which said, 'Keep quiet.'

Milly got the message, her mother didn't want her rocking the boat, and she felt the familiar knot of despair eat at her insides.

–

Milly finished cooking the dinner as quickly as she could. She was silent as she dished up and when she sat down to eat next to her mother.

'What's the matter with her?' Granny O'Donnell asked Bridget, tilting her head toward Milly.

Her mother gave her a look and was about to answer when Milly said, 'I can speak for myself. I've a headache that's all.'

'Another one? I never had a headache, not once when I was your age,' her grandmother said testily. 'We didn't have time for them, that's your trouble, you're too indolent. If you did more work around the house you wouldn't have a headache.'

'I do more than my fair share,' Milly said in outrage. 'Your trouble is that you're old-fashioned and stuck in the past. Why should women be kept indoors doing the housework all the time? In England women are going out to work and making a life for themselves.'

'What tosh!' her grandmother exclaimed. 'I've heard they're trying to take men's jobs from them, being bus conductors and doctors and the like. Whatever next? Perhaps you'd like to drive the tractor and bring in the crops?' Her grandmother laughed unkindly as the rest of the family joined in and Milly felt nauseous as she registered the smirk on Willie's face.

'You just wait,' she said. 'A time will soon come when you'll need us and then we'll show you all what we are capable of, now let me clear the things away.' She could still hear their sniggers as she took the dirty crockery into the kitchen.

–

That night, Milly lay awake listening to her mother's deep breathing and knew that she had had just about as much as she could take.

For years now her life had lurched from one precarious situation to another and the argument with her mother earlier had brought everything back to her. Her mother was harbouring a guilty secret or two and Milly was sure that was why she wasn't sticking up for her where Willie was concerned.

Back in Liverpool her mother had become involved with a man called Mr Chin, who was the boss of the laundry where she worked; not only had she become his lover, she had also had his son, a boy called Charlie. Bridget had also acquired a destructive opium habit that had almost driven her to suicide.

Without the help of kind people in Liverpool, who had gone on to become dear friends, who knows what would have become of them both; Milly knew this was her mother's last chance at respectability. There had been no news of her father, whether he had lived or died, but if he did turn up again, her mother's secret would have to be preserved.

In her heart, Milly knew she had only one choice, if she wanted Willie to stop his torturing of her. She had to get away.

–

She awoke before five o'clock the following morning. Her mother was in a deep sleep beside her and Milly knew she would need to move quickly before the rest of the house started to stir. Every penny she possessed was in a purse that she stuffed into the pocket of her skirt; she had hoarded what little money she could from birthdays and some odd jobs she'd had in the local village and she just hoped it was enough to get her back to England.

The well-worn tweed jacket that had once belonged to her grandmother would keep her warm, as would the woollen shawl that she wrapped round her head and neck.

She would have to make her way to the port at Cobh where hopefully she could catch a ship to Holyhead and then a train on to Liverpool. Milly didn't have a plan yet for what she would do when she got there. Her friends, Anne and Andrew, who had done so much to help her when her mother jumped from a ferry travelling across the Mersey and Milly was left alone, were now in the south of England. But before she could think of that she had to get away from the O'Donnell farm.

Taking one last look at her sleeping mother, briefly wishing that things could be different, Milly pulled the door to quietly and crept downstairs. The house was in darkness, the sun not rising for another hour or so, and Milly slipped out of the back door, to avoid jangling the large, loud bell-pull attached to the front door which would wake the whole house up. Pulling the door shut, she headed out of the cobbled farmyard and away from the O'Donnell farm, knowing she would never return.

–

Milly was lucky and didn't have to walk too far before she was offered a lift by a farmer taking his sheep to market. Milly perched herself on the seat next to him and she was pleased that he didn't talk too much to her on the journey. When he asked her where she was headed, she lied and said she was going to enquire about a job in Cash's department store which she had noticed on a previous visit to the city, having been captivated by its bright window displays of fancy hats and shiny shoes. The farmer seemed to take her at her word.

By the time they arrived in the city centre, the sun was high in the autumn sky. Milly said her thank yous when he dropped her off and trying to get her bearings, she enquired from a passing Garda policeman where she could catch the ferry to England.

He laughed good-naturedly. 'Sure, the boats go from Cobh which is a way out of the city, but there is a bus that you can take, they leave twice a day. If you hurry you can catch the one that goes this morning.' He pointed the way to the bus station and Milly hot-footed it as fast as her legs could carry her, her heavy carpet bag banging against her legs as she ran.

The port bus was loading up its passengers as Milly arrived, breathless, at the bus terminus. The driver helped her with her bag on to the charabanc and took an Irish scilling from her as payment.

As they travelled to the port, Milly wondered at what the O'Donnell family must have made of her disappearance. She had no doubt that her mother would know very well that she had left and why, and she speculated what her mother might have said about her disappearance or if she had kept silent.

Milly felt again the sting of hurt that her mother had not done anything to help her escape from Willie's clutches and to stick up for her. Bridget hadn't been the perfect mother, far from it, but this was a betrayal that Milly found hard to take. She wiped a tear from the corner of her eye and told herself not to succumb to self-pity.

I can look after myself, she thought. I've done it before, and I can do it again.

The journey took over an hour and when they arrived Milly was almost overwhelmed by the amount of people to-ing and fro-ing and the many ships, large and small, loading and unloading passengers and goods.

One couldn't help but feel a little excitement, she thought.

Before Independence, it had been known as Queenstown, and even though it was now known as Cobh, people still referred to the port by its old name, so her mother had told her. Liners travelling from Liverpool to America and back still stopped there, so Milly figured she was bound to get one crossing to Liverpool.

As she queued at the ticket office, Milly hoped she had enough money to make the journey, she only had around two Irish pounds in her purse and knew they wouldn't stretch very far. To her dismay, there were no sailings that day and were unlikely to be so the following day as a storm was sweeping in from the Atlantic, the clerk told her.

'But I have to sail today.' Mildred was suddenly terrified, thinking that Uncle Willie might have followed her and had a vision of him turning up in the horse and cart and dragging her back to the O'Donnell farm.

'I'm sorry, miss, but the crossing won't be safe in a storm, you'll have to wait it out like everyone else.'

For the rest of the day Mildred wandered around the port, drinking in the sights and sounds. That night, she hunkered down with many other passengers who were hoping to sail in the large waiting room. There was a small stove pumping out a little heat and a kiosk selling tea and snacks. Milly didn't think she could afford any food, wanting to preserve the money she had left, but the cups of hot, sweet tea went some way to easing the grumbling in her stomach.

The following morning, tired, stiff and hungry, she was in luck: the storm had blown over and boats were again making the journey to Holyhead. Milly dug deep into her purse and counted out the one-pound fare for the crossing – it was a large chunk out of her money but at least she was putting a greater distance between herself and Willie.

Within a couple of hours, she was on the boat back to England. Milly stood on the deck, feeling the cold blast of the wind and the swell of the waves underneath her; she knew there was an uncertain future in front of her, but for now she was free, and it felt good.

Chapter Three

From the top deck of the ferry boat, Milly had the perfect view across the sparkling surface of the Mersey towards the line of docks that stretched to Seaforth in the north, and to Garston to the south. Although the passage across the Irish Sea had been far from smooth, causing many passengers to spend the voyage hanging over the side of the ship being seasick, she had not been one of them. Even so, she had sent up a prayer of thanksgiving when the ship had crossed the Bar, knowing that her journey would soon be over. At the Bar, there were several buoys in the Mersey indicating where ships had sunk in collisions in dense fog or had been blown onto a sandbank by high winds.

She snuggled her chin deep into her woollen green and red scarf and considered that however attractive County Cork was she preferred Liverpool, and hoped she could find refuge until she could trace her grandmother Adelaide Martin.

She did not doubt that Kyle Anderson, a volunteer at the Seamen's Orphanage would help her. When her mother had been in the infirmary after falling in the Mersey, he had worked hard to reunite Bridget with her Irish family and Milly wondered if he would now be angry with her for rejecting them and coming back to Liverpool with no thought of how she would manage by herself. She thought of her father and that field near a crossroads where the O'Donnell's believed he was buried. She sighed heavily, forcing such sad thoughts from her mind and gazed towards the Liver Building, atop of which were the Liver birds towering into the clouding sky. A lump rose in her throat, tears welled in her eyes and she thought, I'm home at last!

She passed through customs but not before her suitcase was searched and she was asked if she was being met by someone. If she'd had a more innocent upbringing, she would not have nursed the suspicion that the officer was expecting to find the odd bottle of undeclared whisky or packets of cigarettes concealed in her clothing. Since Éire was no longer part of the British Empire, smuggling from the Republic of Ireland was a regular occurrence. She noticed that a priest was also having his baggage searched and kicking up a fuss about it; even so it did come as a surprise to her when the officer withdrew a bottle of whisky from the sleeve of the priest's surplice. The priest insisted that it was a gift from a parishioner and she supposed most people would consider priests and children above attempting to cheat British customs.

It had been a few years since she had been in Liverpool and it took her a little moment to get her bearings, but she was soon making her way to the place where she could catch a tram. But where to she wondered? A tram to West Derby Road would take her within a short walking distance to where Anne's youngest brother, Gordon, lived with his wife, Marjorie. Or maybe a tram that would go along Robinson Street close to Mere Lane where she could find her way to Anne's other brother, Teddy's house. Milly thought that his wife, Maggie, might be glad of some help in the house in exchange for providing Milly with a roof over her head, but how could she just turn up unannounced? It wasn't like they had any attachment to her, like Anne and Andrew did.

There was also Jane, Andrew's half-sister, who she had stayed with for a short time while her mother was in hospital. That had been some years ago now – would Jane still even be at the same house in Ormskirk?

Milly was starting to feel that her plan had plenty of flaws. Despite believing before she left Ireland that she had friends who she could call on, the truth was that these people could well have forgotten her or have no interest in helping her current predicament.

Without thinking, Milly found herself boarding a tram towards Scotland Road. Everton was not only where the Fraser family lived, it was also the stamping ground of the O'Donnell's.

When they were last in Liverpool, Bridget had taken her to visit her cousin Brendon and his wife, Mary. Milly couldn't remember very much about it, and had only ever seen the Liverpool O'Donnell's home once and that had been from the outside. It was in a poor district of the city that sheltered many of the descendants of the Irish who had escaped the Great Famine in the last century, and who had not succumbed to starvation or typhus and who weren't able to afford a ticket to America. She liked her distant cousin Siobhan with whom she had played with in the street outside the houses, which were more like slums than the neat terraces of Mere Lane.

Milly didn't want to get entangled with the O'Donnells who would surely have something to say about her leaving the family farm and might report back to her mother about where she was.

She paid for her tram ticket with an Irish penny which was pretty much like a British one if one did not look too closely. Then she counted the money she had in her coat pocket for the umpteenth time; there was certainly a lot less since she had left Ireland. She would have been penniless if it had not been for her great-grandfather's affection for her. He was far too generous for his own good towards his scrounging brothers and she guessed that was why the farm was so rundown. He had seemed to have expected her to buy a pretty frock with his gift of money at her last birthday, but she had saved it instead and hoped he would not bemoan his generosity when he heard she had scarpered.

She sighed as the tram rattled along London Road, gazing through the window at the shops, when suddenly a memory popped into her head of a wintry morning some years ago when her mother had narrowly escaped being caught shoplifting in the department store, T J Hughes. Fortunately, Milly had noticed they were being watched and had hissed at Bridget and nudged her elbow, sending the box of chocolates tumbling to the floor. Milly had dived for it and placed it back on a shelf before seizing her mother's sleeve and dragging her from the shop.

Bridget had clouted Milly across the head in thanks. 'What did you do that for?' she had snarled at her daughter.

Milly had rubbed the side of her head. 'If they'd caught you stealing, you'd have been fined or sentenced and as we've no money to pay a fine, it would be prison for you.'

Bridget had clouted her again, saying it was for giving her cheek, and Milly had forced down her protestations as she was already embarrassed by her mother and they had been attracting looks on the busy street.

Milly forced down the memory, wondering again at the problems her mother often seemed to attract. What she wouldn't have given for a quiet life; however, that didn't seem to be her lot.

She stepped off the tram on Scotland Road and was surprised to recognise where she was so quickly. The street where the Liverpool O'Donnells lived was nearby but Milly was wary of seeing any of them. Instead she wandered up to the shops and had a look in the windows. There was a chandler's, selling all manner of tin buckets, wooden brooms and many other useful household items.

She was drawn along the parade of shops by the smell of freshly baked bread and found herself outside the bakers with its window presenting an array of sweet and savoury treats. Milly's belly rumbled at the sight of Welsh cakes, Battenberg cakes and Bakewell tarts that looked so delicious. She felt in her pocket for her purse and took out a few pennies.

Inside, she joined the queue and when her turn came, thought for a moment before asking for a slice of Wet Nelly. The favourite cake of Liverpool reminded her of her grandmother and the cosy afternoon teas they used to share. She took a bite of the moist fruit cake and sighed in pleasure.

'I love Wet Nelly too.' Milly heard a voice behind her and turned round to see a girl of similar age with reddish-brown hair and hazel eyes, who looked familiar.

'I haven't had one of these in ages,' Milly said, forgetting her manners and speaking with her mouth full. 'I've been away in Ireland.'

'I have a family in Ireland too, in fact, I think you look a bit like my cousin, Mildred.'

Milly gasped. 'Are you Siobhan? I thought you looked familiar!'

'Yes, I am.' The girl laughed. 'What a piece of luck, meeting each other. I just came up to buy some bread, but what are you doing here?'

'I've come away without telling anyone. I've had enough.' Milly thought it best not to say anything about the reasons why and to keep quiet about Uncle Willie.

'Well, you must come and see your mam's O'Donnell cousins, they don't live far from here,' Siobhan said.

'I don't think I should, I don't want my mother to know where I am,' replied Milly.

'Don't worry about that, Uncle Brendon hated life in Cork. There was a falling out, I don't know what about, but he doesn't talk to many of them now,' Siobhan told her.

Milly was surprised to hear this. Brendon was her mother's cousin and Mary his wife, but she didn't remember a disagreement between them and the Irish O'Donnells or her mother mentioning it. 'Maybe I should come by then. But I have nowhere to stay.'

'Sure, you can stay with us. We'll find a corner for you.'

As they walked toward the street on which the O'Donnells lived, Milly noticed that the houses became more run down and the smart terraces gave way to dirty and decrepit slums. Children in tatty rags played in the streets and men in clogs hung about listlessly on street corners with their flat caps pulled down and their collars turned up. Women wearing aprons and scarves tied in a knot on their heads sat gossiping on their stone steps and eyed her suspiciously.

Siobhan led her down a flight of dirty steps and through the door into the basement of a four-storey Victorian house. The shabbiness and dimness when Mildred entered the dwelling caused her to almost back out in horror before she remembered her manners. A repulsive odour assailed her nostrils which seemed to be a mingling of human sweat and rotten vegetables.

She thought, I'll probably catch some horrible disease and die.

The room she entered was sparsely furnished with a few broken chairs and a shabby sofa that had springs sticking out of it in places. Old newspaper was stuffed into the window frames to keep out the draughts and the floor was bare, no carpet only a few tatty rag rugs. There was an old-fashioned range and a meagre fire burnt in the grate.

'Mary, look who I've found,' Siobhan called out.

Mary was Brendon's wife and she recognised Milly instantly. 'What a surprise! But where's your mother, Bridget?' Mary embraced Milly and looked her up and down. 'My, how you've grown up, what a pretty young woman you are!'

'She's still in Ireland and didn't come with me. I'm going to find a job and look after myself,' Milly told her.

'Does your mother know you are here?' Mary asked her.

Milly hesitated and Siobhan stepped in. 'They had a falling out and you're not to say anything.'

Mary looked shocked, then said, 'The O'Donnells know all about falling out, it's what they are good at. Just wait until Brendon comes home and he'll tell you all about that.'

Mildred became aware that her cousin Liam, who was a burly, yet handsome youth and whom she recognised, was sitting casually on one of the few chairs eyeing her up and down. Mildred didn't like the way he looked at her and turned away. Mary and Brendon's younger children were also running in and out of the house and came nagging at Siobhan for a slice of the fresh bread she had just brought home with her. Milly could hear a baby crying in one of the back bedrooms and wondered how many children Mary and Brendon had.

'Where are your parents?' Milly asked Siobhan as she helped her butter the bread and add scrapings of jam from a jar that was almost empty.

'My mammy is Brendon's cousin, just like your mammy is. I lived in Ireland while my daddy travelled around Ireland and England on the stage. His name is Mick O'Connor and he's Ireland's greatest living baritone.' Siobhan's voice rang with pride. 'I want to go on the stage too and sing.'

'So why are you still here?' Mildred asked.

'Me and me mammy came over here hoping to see me daddy on the stage at the Liverpool Empire, but he'd been and gone by the time we arrived according to the theatre manager.' She handed out doorstep sandwiches to the children. 'Mammy left me here and went off to the Argyle Theatre in Birkenhead, hoping to find news of Daddy there, but that was weeks ago, and she hasn't come back.'

'Why don't you go there and ask after her?' Mildred asked her.

'I haven't the money for the ferry across the Mersey,' said Siobhan.

'You mean your mammy left you here penniless?'

'No, but I had to give some to Mary for my keep and I have to help care for the youngest children as well. I feel sorry for Mary but...' she added in a whisper, 'at least I can escape this place and I can push the pram to the nearest recreation ground in Sylvester Street with the littlest ones.

It's a bit of a job keeping them under control on my own, but the older girl Josie helps out after school. Mary has another on the way.' She whispered meaningfully while looking over her shoulder to check no one could hear her. 'Uncle Brendon doesn't seem to care how many children they have or if they can afford to keep them. It's not what I came to Liverpool for – I want to find my daddy.'

'So, that's two of us with missing fathers,' said Mildred.

'Yours was killed in the civil war, wasn't he?' Siobhan said.

'No one really knows what happened to him, but everyone presumes he's dead,' said Mildred, a catch in her voice.

'What happened to you afterwards?'

'We went to live with my daddy's mother, Grandma Martin, but she and Mother quarrelled too much so we left and she ended up working in a Chinese laundry and shacked up with the owner.' Siobhan's eyes were wide in surprise at this but Milly ignored her and carried on with the story.

'They were kind to us and then Mam got hooked on the dream pipe and had my half-brother Charlie.' She paused. 'After that to cut a long story short, we were on the Mersey ferry, Mam, Charlie and me and...' Milly paused, '...she fell overboard.' Milly took a deep breath.

'Did she drown?'

'Naw, she was rescued by Andrew Fraser and his girl-friend, his now wife, Anne Anderson. She looked after Charlie and me until the police came aboard. Charlie's father came for him and took him home. Mam was taken to hospital and I was taken to the Seamen's Orphanage while she was in hospital. Anne and Andrew continued to take an interest in my and Mam's welfare.'

'Why didn't they get in touch with your grandma?'

'I knew that Mam wouldn't like it. Mam wanted to take me to Ireland to live with her family. Anyway, Andrew gave us the money for the fare and Kyle who was a volunteer at the orphanage escorted us to my great-grandfather's farm in County Cork where several members of the family lived. Mam settled there but I have run away and come back here.'

'Do you think your daddy's dead?' Siobhan asked her.

'I don't know, but I'd love to find him alive.'

'Then we must both keep looking for our daddies.' Siobhan gave Milly's hand a sympathetic squeeze.

At that moment Liam shouted over, 'Come on, girls, don't be talking about us behind our back! What mischief are you hatching over there?'

'We're just talking about our fathers,' said Mildred. 'It's ages since we've seen each other.'

'It's even longer since you've seen me,' he said, 'and you don't appear to be in any rush to hear what I've been doing.'

'That's different,' said Mildred. 'Girls have more to talk to each other about.'

'Gossiping, you mean.' He curled his lip at her. 'Is Joseph, that father of yours, the reason why you're here?'

'Why d'you ask that? Is it that you know something about how he became caught up in the Irish war?'

'How could I? I was only a kid when the fighting was going on.' He grinned sarcastically. 'Your daddy was an eejit getting involved.'

'He must have had his reasons for doing so,' she said, crossly. 'At least he's no coward!'

'You don't know anything about it,' countered Liam.

Mildred hunched her shoulder and turned slightly away, so she could not see his face. 'And what could you know yourself, like you said, you were only a kid.'

'That's where you're wrong,' he said. 'I know more than you think. I heard your daddy was drawn into the fighting by some Irish bloke he'd known while at sea during the Irish Civil War.'

'Who told you that? You're making it up,' Mildred said.

'I heard your mother telling my father, Brendon, when she came here last, she'd had a letter from Ireland which told her that,' said Liam, who seemed to be enjoying Milly's discomfort. 'Why should I lie?' he continued. 'Anyway, if you're not trusting me, ask me pa when he comes in from work.'

'Stop provoking Mildred, Liam.' Mary joined in the conversation, rocking her baby to stop it grizzling. 'Brendon will be home soon from the docks and maybe you can ask him what he knows,' she offered. 'Though not if he's had a few too many. It would be even better if the work was more regular and he didn't drop in at the boozer after he's been paid. He'd arrive home with empty pockets if I didn't send our Josie to hang around outside the pub, saying that we're all hungry, so he hands over some of his money,' said Mary.

'That's because she knows how to turn on the tears,' sneered Liam.

'It's a gift,' boasted Josie. 'What gift can you be proud of?'

'That's enough, the pair of yous,' said their mother wearily. 'Josie, I'm going to need yer help to sort out some space where Mildred can sleep.'

'What about bedding?' asked Josie.

'You'll have to cover yourself with coats. We don't have enough to go around.'

When Brendon arrived home, he was not completely paralytic, but drunk enough to express his pleasure at having his cousin's daughter to stay by pressing sloppy kisses on Milly. She felt like shrinking in a corner.

He ate his dinner of scouse noisily and Milly noticed he was the only one eating a hot meal. The family obviously didn't have enough to share and the children had made do with bread and dripping.

She tried to broach the subject of her father to him, but Brendon did not say anything about his disappearance only mentioning the issue of the money.

'You and your mother'll see us right, won't yer? Yous with yer rich Proddie mother-in-law.'

'What do you mean?' she asked him.

'Sure, your mother will inherit any money that was his as it's over seven years since he went missing, she can ask for a divorce or have him declared dead.'

Milly laughed mirthlessly. 'It's years since I saw me granny Martin, but there's no way she'll allow Mother to get her hands on her money or possessions.'

'Then it would most likely come to you unless Joseph is found to be alive,' Mary ventured.

'That's likely,' Brendon said, finishing his dinner and wiping his mouth on his dirty shirt sleeve. 'Unless she holds you to blame for being dragged away by yer mother.'

'She'll have to make a new will naming you as a beneficiary,' Mary said.

At this, Liam jumped in, 'So you'd be doing your mother out of her money then. Just like all money-grabbing Proddies.'

'I would do no such thing,' Milly said, shocked at the accusation. 'I don't care about any money, only if me daddy is alive or dead.' Mildred felt tears sting at her eyes, she was dog-tired, every part of her ached and all this talk of money and her mammy and daddy was making her head ache.

'That's enough,' Mary said.

'Anyway,' said Brendon. 'Why are ye here without your mammy?'

Milly told him the same story as she had told the others about falling out but didn't say why.

'You're welcome here anyhow – the O'Donnells always stick together, whether they should or not and they have far too much time for that Willie fellow, who's lazy and not to be trusted. I heard some stories about him when I lived at home, I can tell you, but I wasn't thanked for saying me piece. Quite the opposite,' he said.

'Now Brendon, that drink has loosened your tongue. Hush now,' Mary said and started ushering the various younger children to bed. Milly didn't get a chance to ask him what he meant by his comment.

There was only one back bedroom, which seemed to sleep all of the family, and Milly felt her heart sink further, thinking of the bedroom that she'd had all to herself at Grandma Martin's and even of her comfortable bed in Ireland that she and her mother shared. The sheets of which were changed weekly and hung out to dry in the back garden when it wasn't raining, and smelt of the fresh air.

As it turned out she shared a mattress on the floor with Josie, Siobhan and one of the toddlers, they topped and tailed and most of the night she was in danger of slipping on to the cold hard floor. She would have been very cold if she had not kept her coat on, as the army blankets, probably surplus after the war and selling cheaply at the Army and Navy Store, didn't extend far enough to cover her completely. She kept her socks on, too, as Siobhan warned her that there were vermin around and it was not unknown for them to venture forth and nibble one's toes.

Milly wondered why her aunt did not have a cat to keep down the mice, only to be told that the last one had been run over by a motor car on Scotland Road, though they did have a dog in the back yard to keep the rats at bay.

She slept fitfully, her feet becoming icy cold as the fire died in the grate, and she was unsettled by the presence of Liam snoring on the tatty sofa.

–

When they awoke the following morning, Siobhan hissed to Milly to be careful as she got herself ready. 'Liam will pretend to still be asleep but he'll have one beady eye open to catch a glimpse of your knickers.'

Milly had slept in most of her clothes but changed what she needed to under the blankets and coats. That first night had been enough for Mildred and she knew that she couldn't stay at the O'Donnells' for any length of time. Even using the lavvy out the back was a terrible prospect with an outside netty that was used by more than one house. She heard her mother's voice in her head telling her she was spoilt and a snob, though Milly knew this was a hard way to live for anyone, but where could she go next?

Chapter Four

Milly put up with things for a few days more and in that time worked out that neither Brendon nor Liam pulled in a full week's pay. The best either of them could hope for was a few days casual work here and there. The Depression had cut deep in Liverpool; however, there were jobs in the building trade because the Queensway Tunnel under the Mersey was being constructed to ease motor car congestion in the city. There was also a system of slum clearances and new houses being built, but it didn't help the O'Donnell family. Brendon and Liam were dockers and the industry had been mightily affected by the downturn in global trade.

Every day hundreds of men not already in employment would line up for casual work at the docks. Sometimes only a few of them were picked and fights would often break out. Many docking families were struggling and the O'Donnells appeared to be one of them.

'Uncle Brendon didn't use to drink so much,' Siobhan told Milly. 'But since the work dried up, he's looking for solace in the bottom of an Irish whisky glass – drink is the only escape from the life he has.'

'I feel sorry for Mary,' Milly said.

'So do I,' Siobhan agreed. 'Liam is always saying he's going to get some money for the family, but unless it's thieving or begging it's hard to see how.'

One afternoon Milly was sweeping the step at the front and watching the children play in the street when Liam approached the house with a girl about her own age and a young fella who was a year or so older.

Liam leaned against the wall and sneered at Milly. 'Good to see you're working for your keep. Me ma and pa can't afford to keep any old waif and stray that turns up on our doorstep.'

'I'm earning my keep. Who are you to criticise, you aren't bringing in any money. Besides I'm helping Mary with the children.'

'You'll be alright with your rich grandma.' Liam's lip curled in bitterness. 'Then me ma will be forgotten about when you're rolling in it.' He kicked his foot against the step she had been sweeping.

'Yeah, why don't you get back to the bog you came from,' said the girl who was with him.

'Who asked you!' Milly didn't like the girl one little bit, she had a mean face and was wearing a tatty old fur coat and a pair of scuffed court shoes; she was wearing too much make-up with bright red lipstick that had been applied haphazardly on her lips. 'You look like something the cat dragged in.' Milly was determined to give as good as she got.

'Watch how you speak to my Franny now, she's me girl,' Liam said, looking like he might give Milly a thump, though Milly thought she'd give him a thrashing with her broom if he tried it.

The young man who had been silently watching but not saying anything finally spoke up, 'Franny, leave it out, the girl was minding her own business before you piped up.'

'You might be me cousin, but you can stop poking your nose in where it's not wanted.' Franny eyed the young man scornfully. 'You're just a drip, Jimmy.'

Jimmy looked like he had heard this a million times before and didn't rise to the bait. 'That's enough Franny.'

'I'll get in and see me mam and I'll see you later.' Liam grabbed Franny around the waist and ran his ugly fingers down to her bottom which he squeezed lewdly. Milly was disgusted to see that Franny seemed to enjoy it.

'Don't be late if you're taking me to the flickers tonight.' Franny smirked at Milly then sashayed up the street. Liam shrugged in her direction to show he didn't care if he was late or not and then went inside.

Milly looked at the young man, Jimmy. 'What are you gawping at,' she asked.

'I'm sorry about me cousin, she's a bit of a handful. Me mam makes sure I keep my eye on her, but she's a law unto herself.'

'Hanging around with Liam won't do her any favours,' Milly said. 'He might be family, but he's a wrong'un.'

'I know. I'm not dead keen on him myself,' Jimmy said. 'What's your name?'

'Maybe I don't feel like telling you,' Milly teased him a little. He had a nice handsome face and Milly thought it was a kind one too. But his cousin had annoyed her and she wasn't about to let him off the hook. 'I have to get on with my chores.'

The boy seemed torn, but said, 'I need to get after Franny, who knows what she's up to now, she's a right little troublemaker, but she's still family.'

'Go on then, see if I care,' Milly said airily.

'Perhaps I'll see you again?' he offered.

'Oh, I doubt it, I'll be gone soon. Have a nice life!' With that she went inside, and smiled to herself as he gawped after her.

–

Things came to a head later that week when one night, a horrified Mildred spotted a huge mean-faced rat in the cellar, as well as discovering that a couple of her best frocks bought for her by her grandma were missing. When she asked Siobhan where they were, she said she didn't know, and Milly was surprised instead when Mary told her she had pawned them.

'How could you?' Milly said. 'They're the best clothes I have.'

'They are more than we have altogether,' Mary told her, sadly. 'I know it wasn't right of me, but we've no money for even bread to feed the children and little Connor now has a fever and I need money for some medicine. I promise you'll get your dresses back when I get some money to redeem them.'

Milly looked at little Connor who was cradled listlessly in his mother's arms. 'Poor fella.' Despite her annoyance and upset, Milly's heart went out to mother and child. 'I just wished you asked that's all,' she said kindly. Milly felt in her pocket for her purse and took out a few shillings. 'Will that help?'

Mary's lip trembled but she was a tough woman and didn't cry. 'It will, I can afford something now to ease him.'

Besides, Milly thought looking around her, what good are those frocks to me now?

Later that morning, Milly counted out what was left in her purse. She had seven shillings and sixpence left and no matter how many times she looked at it, it remained the same. She had only two options left: try to find her grandmother and throw herself on her mercy, or find digs and get a job. The problem with the latter was that apart from the usual cooking, cleaning and washing, she didn't know how to do anything and Milly had no intention of being a drudge any longer.

—

It was a Monday morning and Siobhan came in carrying all the family's laundry after setting a big pan on the stove to heat the water and wash the clothes in it. Monday was laundry day for mothers and wives everywhere and children not of school age would be slung out on the streets to play while the women of the house took on the heavy work of boiling, scrubbing and rinsing which would take all day. On fine days, the backyards would be full of sheets, shirts and underwear all flapping away, though it could take days to dry clothes indoors when the weather was wet.

'I'll help you with the laundry this morning,' Milly said. 'I'll twist the dolly peg and you can turn the mangle, but after that I'm getting out of here, that rat last night was the last straw.'

'I don't blame you,' Siobhan said. 'If I could find me daddy I'd be leaving too, but I like Mary and Brendon and they've been kind to me, although kindness is all they have to give.'

Milly was in two minds about that, thinking of her nice dresses being hocked down at the pawn shop. 'I have every intention of returning to Grandma Martin's house,' said Mildred. 'I can't stand it here. I think it's a miracle you cope. I feel for Mary and the children having to live in such poverty and squalor and will happily let Mary have the clothes off my back – if I thought it would improve their lives.'

Later that day, Mildred called Mary and Siobhan together and emptied out the contents of the Gladstone bag on the rickety table giving them belongings of her own that she thought would be of use. They included a small hand mirror, another pair of thick woollen socks, and two embroidered handkerchiefs.

Then she kissed them both saying ta-rah, promising to come back and see them.

She was in the mood for exercise, and headed eastwards towards West Derby Road. She had decided to visit Marjorie and Gordon's house where she would enquire about Andrew and Anne, and also about Kyle, who had been so kind to her when her mother was in the infirmary. Marjorie was Andrew's aunt who lived with her husband Gordon and her nephew Robbie who Milly thought must be grown up now. Marjorie was in contact with all the Anderson family. Milly knew that it would be best to tell Kyle that she was back in Liverpool now and maybe he could help her to find a job and somewhere to stay.

She cut through a pretty green space which she remembered as Newsham Park, it was a nice sunny afternoon and there were plenty of people out: mothers in smart belted coats and cloche hats were pushing babies around in tall prams and a band was playing an oom-pah-pah tune on the bandstand. Milly thought again how happy she was to be back. If only she could find her grandmother and her father. As she neared West Derby Road, suddenly, she was unsure of her welcome.

By the time she arrived at Marjorie's home, Milly was dithering with a combination of cold and trepidation. She took a deep breath and rapped on the knocker which offered up no answer. Her heart sank and she was about to walk away when she heard a voice call out, 'Coo-ee!' She turned around and saw a woman heading in her direction accompanied by the sound of her scurrying footsteps. It was not until the figure drew nearer that she recognised Marjorie, who came to an abrupt halt in front of her.

'Is that you, Milly?' Marjorie asked, sounding aston ished.

'Yes, I've been missing Liverpool and decided to come home for a while, but I need somewhere to stay and not having much in the way of dosh, I also need a job. I was hoping to get hold of Andrew or Kyle and that you might put me in touch with one or other of them.'

'But what about your family in Ireland?' Marjorie asked.

'Can I come inside, and I'll try to explain?' Milly said. 'It's cold out here and it feels as if it's about to start raining.'

Marjorie hesitated and then as a gust of wind blew rain in her face, she said, 'Come on in then.'

Milly followed Marjorie inside and along a lobby to the kitchen where a fire burnt feebly in the black-leaded range. 'Sorry, it's not very warm in here,' Marjorie said. 'But we need to make the coal last, what with the short-ages and Gordon's working hours being cut down at the docks. I blame the Americans and the wealthy bankers with their gambling on the stock market. They're a greedy lot, taking risks with men's jobs and not caring about the workers and the poor.'

Marjorie undid her coat and removed her hat, signalling for Milly to do the same and hung them on a hook on the back of the kitchen door. 'So, what about your mam in Ireland?'

'She's fine, but I don't like it in the Cork countryside. I'm a townie and besides… Uncle Willie isn't a good person.'

'In what way?' Marjorie said, concern on her face.

Milly hesitated, not knowing how to put it. 'He… he's a dirty old man, if you know what I mean?' she said.

Marjorie put her hand to her mouth in shock. 'Did you mention it to your mother?'

'I tried,' said Milly. 'I don't think she believes me. She thinks the sun shines out of all the men in the family. Charmers most of them with the gift of the gab, except for Patrick and Callum who spend most of their time with the beasts in the fields. I just need somewhere to stay for tonight and then I'll try and find my grandmother who might take me in.'

'What about the Chinese people you and your mother used to live with?'

'That's out of the question. They'll have forgotten us by now anyhow.'

'Opium and gambling that's what I've heard about the pitfalls of Chinatown,' Marjorie said.

'There's more to the place than that,' Milly said. 'The Chinese are hard workers.'

'Why don't you get a job as a waitress?' suggested Marjorie. 'Or you could be a kitchen maid and wash dishes and prepare vegetables.'

'I'd still need a roof over my head.'

'What about going into service then?'

'I want to do something better than that. There's hundreds of more interesting things for girls and women to do these days,' Milly said, thinking of the cruel jibes from her grandmother in Ireland about what women could and should be doing.

'What about the orphanage, then, where you stayed when your mother was in hospital?' Marjorie suggested. 'Wouldn't they provide you with a bed and board if you volunteered to help out there? Does Kyle know you're over here?'

'Not yet,' Milly murmured, hoping he wouldn't be cross with her after all the trouble he had taken reuniting her and her mother with their Irish relations. 'You're right, though, I could help out at the orphanage.'

She didn't add that she didn't want to do that. It reminded her of a time when she was lonely and afraid and knew it would bring all those feelings back if she was under its roof again. However uncertain life was now, at least she was trying to stand on her own two feet and was no longer at the mercy of her mother's whims.

'You can stay at ours for tonight. Jane will be staying tomorrow night, you remember her, Andrew's half-sister?'

'I like Jane, I stayed with her in Ormskirk and she was kind to me,' said Milly, asking what had happened to Jane since she had last been in Liverpool.

'Her mother Lil left her a small legacy and her cottage in Ormskirk, but she wants to rent it out and live in Liverpool instead. She's lonely and wants a bit more excitement in her life.'

'Where will she live?' Milly asked.

'There's a house coming up for rent in our street,' said Marjorie. 'It's only a few doors away and she's hoping to have a look at it tomorrow. I've spoken to the landlord and I've got the key. Of course, she'll have to pay key money if she decides to rent it, as well as pay a month's rent in advance.'

'That's a lot,' Milly said, thinking of her disappearing seven shillings and sixpence.

'It is, but I doubt she's short of money now she's reunited with her Irish-Scottish grandfather and she'll have the rent from the cottage,' Marjorie said. 'Her grandfather, Doctor Fraser, lives in Northern Ireland.'

'They say my father died in Ireland. He's been missing for over seven years now,' Milly told her.

'It's true that your dad's definitely dead?' Marjorie asked.

'I really don't know for sure, all I know is that he was caught up in the Irish war of Independence in some way. Although it doesn't make sense as he wasn't political as far as I knew. He was a protestant so he could have been on the English side, I suppose.'

'Michael Collins signed a treaty with our government for a free state, didn't he, agreeing to stay loyal to his majesty and the British government?' said Marjorie.

Milly nodded. 'Yeah, but many people said this was a betrayal and wanted nothing less than complete independence. That same day he signed the treaty, Collins said he'd signed his own death warrant.'

'The treaty is what led to the civil war in Ireland,' said Marjorie. 'I read it in the *Echo*.'

Milly sighed. 'Now it seems that Ireland call the English their enemy. If we're their enemy why do so many Irish regard Liverpool as their first port of call when they leave Ireland?'

'They have family over here since way back even before the famine,' Marjorie said. 'Gordon's interested in local history.'

'How are Anne and Andrew? I must give him a call or write to him to explain the situation.'

'They're grand,' Marjorie said. 'Wasn't Anne and Andrew's wedding day lovely? I have to confess that I miss my nephew and his young wife.'

'So do I. I loved being a bridesmaid at Anne and Andrew's wedding. It was the last time I was happy.' She felt a wave of sadness wash over her. 'I never wanted to be a bother to anyone.'

'Ah come on now, Milly, things will look up,' Marjorie said to cheer her up. 'Anne would want us to help you,' she added. 'Anyway, as I've said you can stay at ours tonight because Jane won't be coming until tomorrow.'

Milly's spirits lifted. 'Thanks. I'm grateful. I shouldn't have just turned up the way I did. I tried to make a go of it with the Liverpool O'Donnells but they live in a slum and sold my best clothes. I should have thought a bit harder what I would do when I got here but I couldn't stand it any longer in County Cork. I had hardly a minute to myself. They were always wanting to know where I was and what I was doing on top of the endless chores. They're probably calling me a right little sinner, heading for Hell this very moment for going off without telling them.'

Marjorie said, 'Heaven help us! I take it they're religious.'

'What else?' moaned Milly. 'My Irish grandma had no time for the flickers or film stars, but the stage they like. Apparently one of Mam's cousins married a man who was a comedian and has a lovely baritone voice. He trod the boards at a theatre in Dublin when he was only a youth. His daughter Siobhan has a lovely singing voice too.'

'Fame indeed. Has he appeared here in Liverpool?'

'His daughter believes so.'

'What's his name?' Marjorie asked.

43

'Mick O'Connor if I remember rightly. I never met him.'

'Never heard of him,' said Marjorie. 'Have you any money?'

'A bit.' Milly leaned her chin on her hand. 'My problem is that I look too young to get a proper job yet.'

'I wouldn't be worrying about that right now,' said Marjorie. 'There's still a few jobs around if you don't mind what you do.'

'So, what am I going to do?' Milly asked. 'Sleep in a doorway tomorrow night?'

'The weather forecast isn't good. You could freeze to death,' Marjorie said, looking shocked.

'It wouldn't be the first time,' said Milly. 'And I'd prefer it to staying with the O'Donnell clan. It was damp and smelly in their cellar, there were rats and the men were always drunk or plotting some robbery or swindle.' She shivered. 'I felt sorry for the women.' Her voice broke. 'Maybe I should have put up with Willie's pawing at me instead.'

'You, poor kid,' said Marjorie. 'You've got my sympathy, and we'll worry about the day after tomorrow when it comes, but for now, give me a hand. I want to have Gordon and Robbie's meals on the table for when they come in.'

A relieved Milly stood and helped Marjorie prepare the meal at the sink, scraping the skin off carrots and potatoes, all the while thinking she hadn't told Marjorie half of her story. As her mother used to say some people didn't know they were born, having no idea of how the other half lived.

Milly watched Marjorie stir the contents of the saucepan on the fire in the black-leaded grate. It was almost what her mother called blind scouse, containing mostly potatoes, carrots, onion, and swede with no meat, but Marjorie had found a little mutton in the meat safe and chopped a little of it into the pot.

Marjorie smiled across at Milly. 'This is for Gordon and Robbie there's not enough to go around. We'll make do with a couple of jam butties if that's all right with you and we'll eat them before they come in, washed down with a cup of tea.'

Milly's stomach rumbled and she thought that what she'd love at that moment was a plate of bacon and eggs, but she returned the smile and said, 'I like jam butties, better than bread with no jam at all.'

'I used to work for Nelson's jam factory and love strawberry and blackcurrant jams best, but we're making do with plum this evening.'

'Plums are good,' said Milly. 'Shall I make the butties?'

'That would be a help.' Marjorie waved a spoon in the direction of a shelf where the bread bin was placed with a few jars and tins. 'Cut four doorstep slices and we'll have to make do without butter or margarine. Money is tight everywhere and Gordon has had barely any work these past weeks.'

Milly nodded and cut the bread, spreading the jam straight on to both slices, then placed a plain slice of bread on top of the jammed ones. At least the bread was lovely and fresh with a decent crust on it unlike the cheaper bread that was all the O'Donnells could afford. She remembered when she was much younger and would be sent to the bakery for a fresh loaf. In those days bread was sold by weight and there were times when a loaf would not weigh the full pound and a piece of dough would be added to the top to make up the weight. On the way home Milly would eat that separate piece because she was so hungry, and it always tasted delicious.

She cut the butties into quarters and then placed four on each plate on the table.

'Shall I make a pot of tea?' she asked.

Marjorie nodded. 'Just two teaspoons and a half then fill the teapot with boiling water,' she said, removing the pan from the fire and placing it on the hob.

A few moments later they were seated at the table and eating and drinking. With her mouth half-full, Marjorie said, 'It's a shame that your mother didn't step in for you about what you were going through with your uncle.'

'Mam never listens to me about the stuff that matters to me. I felt bad leaving my English grandmother the way we did. She might have been a bit of a fusspot, but she was good to me and what with her being so disturbed over Daddy, she must have been really hurt when I left with Mam.'

'Surely, you had no choice but to go with her?'

Milly agreed. 'I was only nine. I'd like to see Grandma. She has no other family but me, unlike the O'Donnells.'

'Where did your grandmother live?'

'I'm not sure I can remember. She isn't a Liverpudlian but was born and grew up in a village up Lancashire. Grandfather was a Liverpudlian, though. He owned two shops. When he died, she got rid of one of them and kept the other one on.'

'What about your dad?'

'He ran away to sea and was in the navy during the war and he met Mam when he was on leave. She told me they married before he went back to sea, and the next time he docked he discovered she had returned to Ireland because she didn't have any family and was lonely on her own with a baby. He followed her there and brought her back to Liverpool, but she could never settle for long and went backwards and forwards to Ireland. I never understood how he became involved with the Irish Civil War, only that he wanted me and Mam out of it.' Tears welled in Milly's eyes. 'I have vague memories of the smell of the soap he used and the feel of the bristles on his chin against my cheek.' She sniffed back her tears.

'I think you need to find your grandmother,' Marjorie said.

'I'll do my best but if my mammy finds out she might try and take me back to Cork. God only knows what I'd do if I had to live under the same roof as Willie again,' said Milly, her voice breaking.

'I doubt those over here will know that you're back in Liverpool yet,' said Marjorie, even if they were convinced Milly had run away to Liverpool, coming to get her would take time and money. 'We'll help you find her.'

Milly's slender features lit up and then she sighed. 'Jane's coming here tomorrow, isn't she?'

'Yes, but Gordon or my nephew, Robbie, will be here,' Marjorie said. 'When I explain everything to Gordon, he'll understand and want me to help you and Jane will too if she can.'

'That would be very decent of them,' Milly gratefully acknowledged.

Chapter Five

At that moment, there was the sound of a key in a lock and a few minutes later, Gordon Anderson, brown-haired and with pleasant features, entered the kitchen bringing with him his nephew by marriage, Robbie.

'Is that scouse I can smell?' said Gordon, sniffing.

'Your nose does not lie, husband,' Marjorie said.

'And who's this I can see?' said Robbie. 'If my eyes don't deceive me it's Milly Martin. What's she doing here?'

'She's run away from her relatives in Ireland,' Marjorie said.

Milly burst out, 'I had to escape. I couldn't stand it any longer.'

Gordon let out a low whistle. 'You can't just run away from your family!'

'I've done it,' said Milly. 'And I'm not going back. I'd live on the streets first, but Marjorie said I can sleep here this evening.'

Gordon exchanged glances with his wife. 'I'll explain,' she said soothingly, 'right now, you both go and have a quick wash and a change, then have your dinner.'

Wordlessly, he did as he was told and soon he and Robbie were seated at the table with Marjorie and Milly. Marjorie filled them in on Milly's story while they ate. Both worked as delivery drivers down at the docks, but trade had been seriously affected by the amount of goods coming in and out of the docks.

'Are you sure your grandmother is still alive?' Gordon asked Milly.

'And if she's dead, will you be in clover?' Robbie asked.

Milly flushed. 'I don't want her dead. Or her money, I don't care about that, but if she is, I'll attempt to trace Susan, the maid, she'll know Grandma's solicitor's name and address.'

Marjorie poured them all out another cup of tea and then after handing one to Milly and sitting down, she said, 'Did she have any other relatives or children besides you and your dad?'

'She had a twin brother, but there's a bit of a mystery surrounding him, too.'

'Where did her money come from? Was it from her husband or was it her father who had money?' Marjorie paused.

Milly said, 'Her husband wasn't poor, I told you he was a shopkeeper, but my great-grandfather had a big cotton business and when he died, he left most of it to his wife and Grandma inherited a large sum. When my great-grandmother died, she left everything to be divided between Grandma and her twin, Barnaby, but apparently, if he doesn't make contact by a certain date, his share goes to Grandma. It was the housekeeper, Susan, who told me that when I was much younger.'

'What if he's married with kids somewhere?' asked Marjorie.

Milly shrugged and a sigh escaped her. 'It would be tough on them, wouldn't it? I've heard Mam talking to her mother and aunts about grandmother's house which we used to live in, telling them about the lovely furniture and carpets and curtains, even one of those new-fangled cleaners for sweeping the floor. I remember Susan was suspicious of Mam.'

'Your grandma was fortunate to have domestic help after the war,' said Marjorie.

'Susan's family fell on hard times and Grandma hired Susan and brought her to Liverpool after her own marriage. Grandma's maiden name was Milburn. I picked up bits of the story over the years by listening to them talking of the old days.'

'What about your dad?' asked Robbie. 'Maybe your grandmother will have left instructions that a search be made for him?'

'There's a thought,' Milly said pensively.

'If he is found to be dead, then your mam would inherit as the widow,' Gordon said.

'Not if Grandma had anything to do with it,' Milly reiterated.

'She may not be able to do anything about it. Then there might be nothing to stop the O'Donnells inheriting all that money.' Gordon shook his head.

'Anyway, first things first,' said Marjorie. 'Let's see if we can trace your grandmother, can you remember anything at all about where she lived?'

'A place called Stanley Park rings a bell,' Milly said.

'I reckon enough said for the moment,' intervened Gordon.

Silence fell except for the crackling of the fire and when the meal was over the conversation was not resumed.

–

Milly slept fitfully that night, but even so she was up bright and early the following morning and counting her money yet again thinking she really would have to get some work very soon. She was delighted to find there was an indoor bathroom in Marjorie and Gordon's home which she hadn't remembered from the last time she was there and thought they must have changed one of the upstairs bedrooms into one. It was a relief not to have to go outside on such a cold morning to an outdoor privy. Or to share it with half a dozen other families like the Liverpool O'Donnells had to.

Milly heard voices below and came downstairs to see who it was. She was very pleased to see a face she recognised; Jane Fraser rose from the sofa and smiled at her.

'How lovely to see you Milly, my how you've grown. How old are you now?'

'I'm fourteen,' Milly said.

'Well, you're quite the young lady.'

Milly stared at the finely drawn features framed in wavy fair hair. She noted that Jane's figure was still slender, just right for the current fashions. Milly felt childish and unworldly, in comparison, with her hair in plaits and her dowdy country clothes.

'Robbie and Gordon have been telling me about your troubles, Milly, and I thought that maybe you could help me move and lodge with me if we don't have any luck finding your grandmother.'

'I'd like that,' said Milly enthusiastically.

'More to the point,' said Marjorie. 'What did you think of the house at number fifteen, Jane – will you move in?'

'It needs some work on it, but it will do me,' Jane said. 'Milly, Ormskirk was all very well, but I need to find a job and I've more chance of finding something in Liverpool. Come upstairs with me and help me unpack.'

In the bedroom upstairs, Jane opened her small suitcase and took a few of her toiletries out, her hairbrush and a nightie and while she did so, she and Milly talked of all that had passed in the intervening years since they had last seen each other.

Jane had lived quietly in Ormskirk she told Milly, and had been stepping out with a young man who was a local baker, but the relationship had fizzled out.

'He always fell asleep, Milly. Every time we went to the pictures, I'd hear him snoring beside me. It was all those early starts.' They both laughed. 'Made me realise I'd like a man with more get-up-and-go about him.'

'You've lovely things.' Milly admired the fine silk blouse with puffed sleeves and the navy drop waist skirt that Jane was wearing. 'You look very sophisticated.'

Jane cocked her head to one side and regarded Milly for a moment. 'You're a pretty girl, Milly, and should make a bit more of yourself. I've a few old blouses and skirts that you can have, they'll be more fashionable than the country attire you're dressed in.'

Milly looked down at the sensible tweed skirt she was wearing and the thick cotton shirt that was good for scrubbing vegetables in and not much else.

'We must get your hair cut too, those plaits are for a little girl Milly, not a chic young lady that we must turn you into.'

'I love those romantic waves you have in your own hair,' Milly said admiringly, thinking of her own untameable tresses.

'Then you must have them too, but not just yet, we want your grandmother to recognise you!'

Jane had offered to come to Stanley Park to look for Milly's grandmother's house with her and Milly felt that she should offer to pay for Jane's fare as she was doing her a favour. As it was, Jane refused her offer, pushing the coins back into Milly's hand and suggesting they make the journey on foot to see if anything would jog Milly's memory.

They were in luck, as it didn't take them long for Milly to recognise the street where her grandmother used to live, but Milly wasn't sure which house it was as they all looked the same.

Jane saw a maid in a neat pinafore scrubbing the front steps of one of the houses which were large and well-maintained with spotless net curtains in all the windows. Jane asked after a Mrs Adelaide Martin and fate was smiling on them as the maid told them that Mrs Martin had moved to Waterloo, near Crosby beyond Bootle and even gave them the address.

Jane insisted on paying for the tram fare. The journey did not take them long and Milly enjoyed gazing down at the shops from the upper deck of the tram and watching people passing by. They changed trams and finished their journey at the site known as the Five Lamps where there was a monument to the local men who had sacrificed their lives in the Great War. They walked the rest of the way to Great Georges Road where the Victorian town hall was situated. The houses were large, mainly detached and all had large front lawns with neatly trimmed grass. Milly didn't think she had ever seen such nice houses and felt nervous as they walked up the path to the front door, ringing the bell which they heard jangle loudly on the other side.

After a short wait, it was opened by a woman with light brown hair and slender features who looked to be in her mid-twenties and whom Milly recognised despite the years that had passed since they had last seen each other.

Even so there was a questioning note in Milly's voice, 'Susan, is that you?'

The maid stared at her intently and said, 'Goodness, is that you, Miss Milly?'

'Yes! It's good to see you, Susan. How is my grandmother, is she able to see me and my friend Miss Fraser?'

'Of course, I've her up and dressed, but you'll find her very changed, Miss Milly.'

'I'd expected that. She'll be getting on now.'

All this time they had been standing on the doorstep and a chill wind was fluttering their headscarves.

'Let us in, please,' said Jane. 'Or we'll catch our deaths out here.'

Susan stepped aside and opened the door wide. 'The mistress isn't that old, but she's muddled sometimes. The doctor thinks it's the strain of the last years – her brother and her son missing, as well as falling out with your mother and not seeing you. She had a terrible bout of the flu and was lucky to make it through at her age. Luckily it wasn't half so bad as the Spanish flu that killed millions.'

Milly and Jane looked at each other; the Spanish flu had laid waste across Europe over a decade ago and it was still fresh in people's memories. It had come just after the Great War and men who had returned alive after the horrors of the trenches were cruelly cut down by the epidemic. Everyone knew someone who had died, and it had affected young adults more than the very young and the elderly.

'Sometimes she doesn't know what's real and what isn't. It could be that she won't know you, Miss Milly.'

'Well, let's see, shall we?' Milly said. She and Jane entered the house behind Susan, who pushed open the vestibule door and entered a black and white tiled hall. Straight ahead was a staircase. 'Is she up there? You said you had her up and dressed. Is she still in her bedroom or having her breakfast?'

'In the morning room, just here. She never eats much these days, so is just having a cup of tea and a couple of slices of thinly-cut buttered toast,' said Susan, going ahead and opening the door to the morning room for Milly and Jane.

Milly stepped inside, the walls were painted duck-egg blue and the room was full of sunshine. She stared at the hunched figure sitting at a small table, facing them. It was not so much the wrinkled face that caused tears to spring to her eyes but the lack of fire and determination in the washed out pale-blue ones that stared back in her direction. 'Grandma?' she said gently.

The pale-blue eyes moved and fixed on Milly's face. 'Louise!' she said.

Milly remembered her grandmother had had a cousin, Louise, but she had died shortly before Milly and Bridget had left. 'No, Grandma. I'm your granddaughter, Milly.'

'Milly?' The old woman seemed to taste the name with her tongue and roll it round her mouth repeating it several times.

'I'm Joseph's daughter, your son.' Milly drew up a chair beside her grandmother and placed an arm around the narrow bony shoulders clad in a Fair Isle cardigan over a cream silk blouse. 'Mam took me to Ireland, but now I'm back.'

'Bridget – that cat!' Adelaide Martin screwed up her face and pouted her lips.

Milly smiled to herself, that her grandmother remembered her mother so vividly was a good sign.

'Ireland… You went there to find my Joseph, didn't you? I was told he was dead but he's just missing.' She reached up a trembling blue-veined hand and placed it over that of her granddaughter's that rested on her shoulder. 'You must find him.'

The words *he could be dead* echoed in Milly's mind, but she couldn't bring herself to say them out loud, not knowing the effect they might have on her grandmother. The old woman's fingernails dug into Milly's hand. 'You have to find him. I'm lost without him. Just as I was lost without my brother Barnaby when he went missing.'

'You have Susan to help you. She's been faithfully serving you for years.'

'I know.' Adelaide stared at the maid and smiled. 'She's a good girl, but I need my son. People take more notice of a man. You'll have to go back to Ireland and find Joseph. I thought he would have found Barnaby by now, even though it's a long time since he ran away.' She bit into a slice of toast and except for the crunching as she ate a silence descended in the room.

Jane stared at Milly and then they both looked at Susan. 'I think we need to talk further, Susan,' said Milly in a low voice. 'Can we leave Grandma for a short while?'

Sue nodded. 'I'll just refill her cup and she'll be all right. I'll tell her I'm just going to do some polishing while you two go to the shops, and we'll be back soon.'

She did so; Adelaide nodded and waved as they rose and left the room. Susan led them to the sitting room where

Milly and Jane sat down on a sofa. Milly indicated that Susan be seated too.

'How long has Grandma been this way?' asked Milly.

'Her doctor has visited her several times and it was he who advised I get in touch with the mistress's solicitor. I did so, and they put their heads together and had a natter. Apparently, your mother, Bridget, has written to him informing him that she is asking the courts to have your father declared dead. She has a good cause to have them agree to this, him being missing so many years. The solicitor has told Mrs Martin this, but it has only made her obsession with your father's fate worse and she is ignoring the possibility that he is dead. She says he must be found. She is refusing to alter her will or make any change in this regard. Before your mother's actions, she was considering making a new will leaving most of her money to you, Miss Milly, and a small legacy to me but recently she had a vision of Mr Joseph in which he speaks to her, and now it's all she can talk about.'

'What did he say in the vision?' Milly asked.

'Apparently, he asked her to forgive him. The thought that he is alive somewhere is what is keeping her going, saying she needs to tell him to his face that she would forgive him anything – I spoke to my own mother about it, who remembers the circumstances and she said that when the mistress's twin, Master Barnaby, went off, she went all fey as well, believing that he was getting in touch with her by telepathy, what with them being twins. He was letting her know he was still alive, so she could tell their mother who was sick with grief.'

'It is possible that he is alive,' said Jane slowly. 'Think of the Great War. Hundreds of thousands of men were buried en masse then and some men who were declared missing later turned up alive. Maybe it is the same for the Irish Civil War?'

Hope stirred inside Milly before she checked herself. 'But it's years since we were told Daddy was thought to be dead. The Irish Civil War ended in 1922. That was around ten years ago. If Daddy were alive, surely he would have been in touch by now.'

'What if he had a head injury and had lost his memory and wandered off,' Susan said breathlessly. 'I read a story once where something like that happened.'

'You can't believe everything you read in a penny dreadful,' said Jane who was a no-nonsense person.

'I suppose it is possible,' Milly murmured. 'What if he had still been alive when they buried him, only stunned, and dug himself out?' She shuddered at the thought.

Jane placed an arm around her. 'Calm down, Milly. These are only thoughts. We've no proof.'

'No, but I'm going to have to do what my grandma said and try to find out what happened to him.' Milly wrung her hands. 'Maybe I should go to Ireland.'

'Out of the question,' said Jane. 'How far do you think you'd get?'

'But I must.' She stood up and stamped her foot. 'Oh, how I wish Andrew and Anne were here. They would know what to do.'

'Who are Anne and Andrew?' asked Susan.

'A married couple who are great friends of mine,' said Milly. 'But they're down south in Essex. He's a journalist and knows how to find out things and she's good at searching out the truth.'

'You're forgetting about Kyle Anderson. He could help you, too,' Jane said. 'He's been to Ireland.'

'Who's Kyle Anderson?' Susan asked, a bewildered expression on her attractive little face.

'A member of the family, related to my brother's wife's family, the Andersons,' said Jane.

'We can't tell the mistress all this,' Susan said. 'She'll be even more confused.'

'Then we tell her only that we're getting some friends to help us find Joseph,' said Milly. 'Best she carries on hoping and wishing that he's alive than she sinks into misery again and loses her mind completely.'

'So, our next step is to telephone Andrew,' said Jane. 'We'll have to be going now anyway, we've been out long enough.'

Milly nodded. 'Just let me say ta–ra to Grandma.' Milly went into her grandmother's morning room and placed a gentle kiss on her forehead. 'I'm so glad I've found you, Grandma.' Milly meant it.

'You will find your father for me, won't you Milly dear?'

Milly squeezed her grandmother's hand and prayed that she could.

Chapter Six

As Milly and Jane entered the kitchen back in Liverpool, Marjorie rose from the sofa and smiled at them. 'How did you get on? Is your grandmother well, Milly?'

'As well as can be expected given her age – she has some strange thoughts. She believes Daddy isn't dead, just missing and wants me to return to Ireland to find him.'

Gordon who had just entered the kitchen gave a low whistle. 'Difficult! So, what are you going to do?'

'Nothing until I've spoken to Andrew and Anne. I'm going to telephone them this afternoon and ask them their opinion on some of the things we discussed about the situation,' Milly replied. 'Of course, I'd be interested in what you, Jane and Robbie think, too.' She told them of all the things that Susan had said about her grandmother and the will.

'And you trust this Susan?' said Gordon.

Milly nodded. 'She's been loyal to my grandmother all these years.'

'Then let's talk over dinner,' he said. 'We've been hanging on until you came in before eating.'

Within half an hour the food was dished out and they were sitting around the table. Everyone was hungry and nobody spoke until they were halfway through the meal.

Gordon said, 'I suppose it's possible your father is still alive, Milly. He could have slipped away during a lull in the firing from the other side and hidden behind a tree or a rock if this happened in the countryside.'

'It happened at a crossroads but there was a lot of deserted countryside and scattered hamlets, farms and the like in the area, I was told,' said Milly. 'But surely if he did so he would have been in touch if he was still alive.'

'Whose side were the O'Donnells on during the civil war?' asked Jane.

'The other side to Daddy. I think he was for the treaty that was signed with the British government giving Ireland some self-government but remaining in the empire. They were against. Mammy said it was another reason they took against him,' Milly replied, sucking her fingers after gnawing the meat from the bones of the breast of lamb before wiping her hands on her only hand-kerchief. 'Many brothers and cousins fought against each other in the civil war, it tore the country apart.' She told them again about the ambush after which he was never heard of again.

'If he's not dead, I reckon he must have lost his memory or he doesn't want to be found for some reason,' Robbie said.

'Me, too,' said Jane. 'He must have had some help, though, to have survived if he's done so.'

'But why would my daddy not want to be found?' Milly questioned. 'Surely he'd want to see me.'

'Maybe he's involved in criminal activity and doesn't want to end up in jail. He could be a fugitive from justice,' Robbie suggested with an excited glint in his young face.

'Nonsense! My daddy wasn't a scoundrel. He was a good man,' Milly said, incensed at Robbie's suggestion.

'Don't take on so. I'm only thinking out loud. Maybe, if the ambush had happened not far from the coast, he

stowed away on a ship and managed to sneak ashore somewhere else.'

'Could be in Scotland or Liverpool, the Isle of Man or
even Northern Ireland,' said Jane.

Milly responded with a touch of anticipation. 'The
sooner I telephone Andrew and Anne the better – and
I've just remembered something, Mammy told me that
the news about Daddy was sent from an Irish sailor he'd
known during the Great War.'

'Didn't you tell us that your dad was a sailor for a while,'
Gordon said. 'They must have served on the same ship. Do
you know if he was in the Royal or Merchant Navy?'

Milly's brow knitted in thought. 'I think when he first
went to sea, he was in the merchant navy, but during the
war he might have joined the Royal Navy. My grandma
will know if she can remember,' she said.

'You should ask her,' Gordon suggested. 'For all we
know your dad might have come back to Liverpool to
sign on to a ship and gone to your grandma first, only to
discover that she'd moved.'

'Possibly,' said Jane. 'That setback might have confused
him, and he might have then returned to the waterfront
and joined a ship.'

'You've got to remember that we're in the middle of
a Depression and loads of men are laid off and there are
less ships arriving and departing,' said Gordon. 'Although,
there are those old salts who hang around smoking their
pipes and talking of old times who might recognise him
by a description, if he did come to Liverpool.'

'I do have a photograph,' said Milly. 'Right now, I'm
going to telephone Andrew and Anne.' She wasted no
time leaving the house and going in search of a kiosk on

West Derby Road. Jane accompanied her as she was keen to have a few words with Andrew herself.

It took a while to put a call through to him but eventually they heard his pleasant tenor voice come down the line. Both Milly and Jane craned the receiver between them so that they could both hear and speak to him. To say he was surprised to hear what Milly had to say was an understatement, but he did not quash her hopes that her father Joseph could still be alive and promised to get in touch with several people on the off chance, including the Seaman's Mission who might have heard of a man answering Milly's father's description.

'If he escaped from the fighting in the south of Ireland, he could have been wounded and it is possible that he lost his memory. I'll add that I know it's a long shot, but that his daughter and his mother are desperate to know the truth about what happened to him. One never knows. Seamen are a tight-knit lot, and someone might have heard something over the years.'

'Grandad Fraser might also be able to help, I think,' Jane put in.

'I agree,' Andrew said. 'It's unlikely that he knows or has heard anything specifically. He has lived in Northern Ireland near the coast for most of his life but him being a doctor means he'll know others in the profession who just might have come across people like your father, Milly, if that is what happened to him. He could help us with understanding Joseph's state of mind.'

'Could the police help?' asked Milly.

'That's unlikely, both sides of the fight would be wary of the authorities, there was a lot of illegal activity such as gun-running and smuggling that went on.' He paused. 'Is there anything else you want to mention? Have you been in touch with Kyle about what is going on?'

Milly said, 'Not yet, but I will. My mother is bound to write to the orphanage, so I need to give him some warning.'

Andrew urged caution, saying to Milly that if her father had wanted to be found, then there would have been some word of him in the last decade. He also had some good news and told them that Anne was expecting their first child. Both Jane and Milly cooed down the receiver and told him to give Anne their love. After a few words with Jane, they both said goodbye.

Milly and Jane returned to the house and told the others what Andrew had to say and not long after they called it a night and went to bed. Jane having the spare bedroom and Milly sleeping on the sofa.

–

The wind had increased, and so Milly and Jane were wrapped up warm when they left the house the following morning. They had planned on visiting the orphanage before they both caught the train to Waterloo to visit Milly's grandmother but as it happened, they did not need to visit the orphanage because Kyle dropped by at Marjorie and Gordon's house in his delivery van, just as Milly and Jane were leaving.

Kyle had been an orphan child himself and as a young boy he had found a safe haven there, so he had decided to give something back when he was able and volunteered as a helper. He had looked out for Milly when her mother was taken to the infirmary after jumping into the Mersey and Milly thought of him like a big brother. She knew that she should have been in contact with him before now, and it was understandable that he demanded to know what was going on.

He gazed at Milly intently. 'What on earth's happening? Why are you over here?'

He told them he had been at the orphanage the evening before when there had been a telephone call from Ireland to one of the guardians enquiring whether Mildred Martin, a former resident, had called in there and then the caller had asked for Kyle's home address.

'I took the telephone call and it was your mother, Bridget. Luckily I could answer her truthfully that I hadn't seen anything or heard from you for months. Then I caught the sound of a man's voice in the background asking about your friends, Anne and Andrew. I thought that was odd,' said Kyle. 'Even so I said that I hadn't heard from them in an age either. Then Bridget asked whether I could let her have their telephone number and address as well. I told them I didn't have it with me and ended the call. Can you explain yourself?'

Milly said, 'It's a long story, Kyle, and I know I should have explained before now, but I don't have time. Jane and I are off to visit my grandmother in Waterloo and then to Jane's cottage in Ormskirk.'

'I can give you a lift into town. I'm going that way. You can tell me yourself then.'

They followed him over to the van and he helped Milly up first and then Jane who could help herself, although she couldn't help smiling warmly into his attractive features. It wasn't the first time they had met, but it had been some years before and she thought he had matured into an even more handsome fellow. She had always admired him for his kindly nature and his willingness to put in unpaid hours at the orphanage, as well as for his good looks and his well-honed physique.

As soon as the vehicle was in motion, he asked Milly to tell him everything. She wasted no time in doing so, although several times she paused, and it was Jane who found the words the girl couldn't, without feeling embarrassed, to recount the story about Uncle Willie.

'I can understand why you don't want to go back, then.' Kyle's features were dark. 'The man's a scoundrel and your family should have drummed him out of the house. If I could get my own hands on him…'

'They didn't know, only my mother and that's why I'm here. I'll never go back, they can't make me. I'm almost a grown woman and capable of looking after myself.'

'Good for you,' Jane said. 'There's something else that Andrew told us, Anne's in the early stages of pregnancy.'

'That's marvellous news, so they won't be travelling anywhere for a while. That aside,' said Kyle. 'Is there anything I can do to help?'

'Let us know if anyone comes looking for Milly at the orphanage,' said Jane. 'It would be useful, though, if we could visit you at home sometimes, instead of there. It's the first place they'll come looking for her.'

'That's fine by me,' he said, waiting until he had parked as close to Exchange Station as he could, before jotting his address down with a stub of pencil on a scrap of paper and handing it to Jane. 'You'll keep me posted with any more news?' He looked at her keenly.

'Will do,' Jane said, taken by surprise at the thrill that passed through her as their fingers brushed.

She and Milly said their farewells and watched for a few moments as he drove off in the direction of the docks before they went inside the station. They were both silent

66

for a while and did not speak until the train was past Bootle, then Milly said, 'Do you think it wrong of me to expect help from so many of my grown-up friends when it means going against my family wishes?'

'Who else would you turn to? And you wouldn't be the first girl to run away from home.'

Milly pounced on her words. 'The house in Ireland never felt like home. Even the house in Pitt Street in Chinatown had something about it that made me feel less of an outsider despite all that was wrong about what went on there. No doubt that must sound strange to you, but there I was accepted for who I was and, of course, there was my half-brother Charlie who I was so fond of.'

'What are your plans for the future?'

'I've finished with school. I didn't go in Ireland but helped in the house and the fields. I need to find a job now.'

'Have you got any skills besides housework?'

Milly's face dropped knowing that she hadn't. 'I'm a fast learner. Sure, I could put my hand to anything. There must be something better out there than cooking, washing and cleaning. Women can do all sorts now.'

'They can,' Jane said wisely, 'but you have to learn and apply yourself. There's lots of girls like you and not so many jobs these days. Gallivanting off looking for your father won't help with that.'

'It's not gallivanting!' Milly answered crossly. 'Looking for me daddy is something I must do.'

'That won't be easy and you need something to live on, you said yourself you can't rely on anyone else.'

Milly did not argue, knowing Jane had a very good point, only saying, 'Let's wait and see what Grandma has to say. If she wants me to help find her son and her brother, I will, but I can't do it on fresh air.'

The subject was dropped and no more was said about it on their journey to Waterloo which was north east of the city.

–

Over tea and homemade scones, Adelaide took to Jane after hearing that she had lived in Ormskirk for years; the village where Adelaide had been brought up was not far away from there. She seemed to understand that Milly had enlisted several friends to help find Joseph and she spoke through a mixture of tears and smiles when she talked of her husband Reginald and how happy they had been when Joseph was born.

'He had been such a handsome baby,' she said.

Jane did not consider it odd that Adelaide should remember some things clearly but be confused over others as her own mother had been the same as she aged.

It seemed though, that Adelaide was more aware of the situation than either of them realised because she said to Milly, 'If you aren't here with your mother, then where are you living and with whom?'

Milly looked a little awkward. 'I've been sleeping on a friend's sofa up until now, but I'm going to help Jane move house, and then she is going to let me stay with her.'

'But Jane cannot afford to keep you and you do not have a job.' Adelaide astutely observed. 'Do you have a job yourself, Jane?'

'Not yet,' Jane answered. 'I've applied for a job in a hat shop and they are just checking my references. I hope I shall be able to start soon.'

'Mildred, if you are to help me find Joseph, then you must live with me. I have been without family for some time now and you will be a great comfort to me.'

Milly and Jane smiled at each other, knowing this was the perfect solution to the situation.

'I've promised to help Jane move house, Grandma, so I will come when we have done that.'

—

Soon after they left the house. Milly promised to return in the next couple of days and was filled with relief that her situation now seemed less precarious. With her grandmother's support, Milly thought her chances of living an independent life were looking up. They caught the Southport train where they connected to a train destined for Manchester that stopped at Ormskirk.

Despite her concern for her grandmother and whether the hunt for her father would prove a wild goose chase, Milly enjoyed the journey and felt relaxed in Jane's company, thankful that they could be real friends and that she was no longer imposing on Jane's good nature. Eventually the train pulled into Ormskirk station and they set off to walk to the cottage. In no time at all the fire was lit, the bed was made up in the spare room and Jane had a hotpot in the oven. She was soon making a list of the furnishings she could take with her to Liverpool and those she would leave behind for the tenants who would rent the cottage from her.

Milly gazed about the room which was furnished with a heavy Victorian dining set and two fireside chairs, the backs of the latter which were hung with embroidered antimacassars. She guessed that the furniture had come from an elderly relative.

'So, as your grandmother noticed, you're in need of employment Milly. Looking for missing relatives won't keep you long and you need to think about what will happen after that's all over. Fortunately, I have some experience of shop work and have had an education and I also have money in the bank.'

'Lucky you,' said Milly. 'What I would like to learn is typewriting, then I could work in an office.' Milly had found a copy of the *Woman's Weekly* on a bench in the ticket office when she was at the station and flicking through it, she had seen an advertisement for women to learn shorthand, dictation and typing. She loved the idea of sitting at a desk and firing off letters on a typewriter and could imagine herself working in the office of a factory or even at Liverpool Town Hall.

Jane hesitated before saying tactfully, 'Fair enough, but you'd need to know the alphabet and to do basic arithmetic, and how to set out a business letter. What about practising by writing to your mother assuring her that you are safe and well?'

'I know my alphabet and arithmetic from the church school I attended when I lived with Grandma. Why bother with my mammy? She's already telephoned the orphanage, so thinks I will have come to Liverpool. The less she and the O'Donnells know the better, they'll want to drag me back there.'

The thought of learning to type made Milly feel hopeful. She could read and write, add and subtract, sew and make simple meals and had quite a decent singing voice. Of course, she could try getting into a night school where they taught typing. She had heard of a technical and commercial college called the Mabel Fletcher, so perhaps they would accept her. She would have to pay for the lessons and hoped her grandmother would give her enough money. Then Jane changed the subject, and talked about Anne and Andrew down south. 'Andrew asked me to look up their neighbour's sister whom they had met when she visited Southend occasionally. I thought I might do that next weekend.'

'I don't mind going with you,' Milly replied, draining her teacup to the dregs. 'I suppose we'd better get on with the packing.'

There were two rear bedrooms that were unoccupied in the cottage. Jane having the larger front bedroom. The smaller of the two was being used as a storeroom as there were a couple of tea chests in there and a cupboard; the other had a single bed, a chest of drawers, an ottoman and a plain wooden chair.

'Will this do you?' Jane asked. 'There's bedding in the ottoman.'

'It's fine,' said Mildred. 'I really do appreciate everything you are doing for me.'

'I miss Lil. It's nice having your company again.' And Jane left Milly to make up her bed.

Milly smiled, thinking Jane sounded as if she really meant it and that made her feel warm inside. Milly lifted the lid of the ottoman and removed some bedding and wasted no time in making up the bed. She was just about to dive beneath the covers when there was a discreet knock on the door. 'Come in,' she called.

Jane entered, carrying a hot water bottle. 'I thought you might like this,' she said.

Milly took the hot water bottle made from stone with a delighted expression. 'You are kind to me,' she said.

'It isn't difficult to show a little kindness to people,' Jane said. 'Lil was a great believer in a little kindness going a long way in making friends.'

'Anne was kind to me from the first moment we met on the ferry on the Mersey,' said Milly.

Jane said. 'Anyway, enough talk. We've got to start packing all the boxes up and getting ready for the move the day after tomorrow, then we've to put all the things away at the house in Liverpool. There's a lot to do.'

'You mustn't worry about that,' said Milly, snuggling down beneath the covers and pushing the hot water bottle further down with her feet. 'I know how to roll my sleeves up and get stuck in.'

'We need a good night's sleep,' Jane said, thinking of all the lugging around they would have to do tomorrow, she hoped they could manage it. 'Anyway, goodnight, God bless.'

'Same to you,' Milly said sleepily.

Jane tiptoed out of the room and closed the door, praying Milly was not taking on too much in looking for her father. Still, if nothing else life was not going to be dull having Milly around again.

Chapter Seven

Milly was already up and about when Jane awoke to see her standing at her bedside with a tray bearing a cup of tea and a plate of buttered toast and marmalade.

'Good morning,' whispered Milly. 'I thought you might like breakfast in bed.'

'Thanks, but you'll be spoiling me.' Jane sat up, dragging her pillow up behind her back.

'I thought you deserved a treat for all you've done for me and you must keep your strength up today.'

'Agreed,' Jane said. 'At least we're both up early to get the packing done.'

Milly said, 'I've already started and have been packing the kitchen items into one of the chests. There's a lot of dust in the corners of the rooms which I've been sweeping up. I had a lot more to clean when I was living in Pitt Street so I'm used to it.'

'I don't want you skipping the corners. I'll be checking. I can't abide spiders, cockroaches or bugs or mice. My mother, Lil, waged war on them,' said Jane, reaching for her cup of tea. 'I've been thinking further about your idea to learn typing, you may need paper qualifications to get into night school or at the least a reference from your school.'

'There must be another way of learning typing without all that paraphernalia,' complained Milly.

'Well, if you can come up with one let me know,' said Jane.

'I need someone who can teach me privately who could get me up to scratch to earn a place at the Mable Fletcher College in Liverpool. Someone who could do with extra money and is a good typist,' said Milly.

Jane looked thoughtfully as the girl left the bedroom and wondered how they would find someone like that.

They spent the rest of the day packing up the contents of the house and luckily for Jane the spiders were nowhere to be seen.

–

The following morning Jane enjoyed breakfast in bed again, courtesy of Milly, but there was no time to luxuriate in it. She gobbled down the tea and toast, and washed in cold water in the bowl on the washstand.

She emptied the dirty water in the slop bucket and hurried downstairs where she found Milly dressed in just knickers, vest and liberty bodice, washing her face and neck at the sink in the back kitchen. Then the girl started feeling around, her eyes shut, for something to dry her face with. Jane fetched the towel that they had left out for that purpose and not packed away, thrusting it into the girl's hand.

'Thanks,' Milly said, drying her face, then her ears and neck and quickly got dressed. Jane was plaiting Milly's hair when the door knocker sounded shortly after. When Jane answered the door, she was surprised to see it was the removal man's young apprentice from Ormskirk. She was expecting them to arrive a bit later, but he had unwelcome news for her.

'The van's broken down outside Southport and the boss can't fix it,' he said, fiddling nervously with his flat cap.

'Where does that leave us? We're ready to leave this morning and the new tenants are moving in later on today.' Jane was normally a very calm and sensible person but was upset as she had no idea how they would find someone at short notice. 'When will the van be fixed?' She enquired angrily, though she knew it wasn't the boy's fault.

'No idea, miss, the engine's blown a gasket.'

Jane didn't know what to say that could be repeated in decent society and was about to let loose with an angry tirade when a welcome face appeared behind the young apprentice and to her delighted surprise it was Kyle. 'What are you doing here?' she asked.

'I woke early and got to thinking,' he replied. 'If you're moving to Liverpool, you're going to need a man to give a helping hand with the heavy stuff.'

Jane could scarcely believe it. 'You're offering to be that man?' she said. 'You couldn't have come at a better moment, the removal van has broken down.'

The delivery boy, sensing a reprieve, took this moment to scarper.

'It must have been fate.' Kyle gave her a winning smile. 'I do have a mate who has a bigger vehicle than my work's van that I'm sure he'll let me borrow for a few bob and the cost of fuel.'

'That sounds a good deal,' she said. 'How much for your work?'

'Tea and homemade scones one evening with your good self,' he said with a wink.

She blushed, thinking how could she possibly refuse such an offer after he had been so generous? She thanked him and he told her he'd be back as soon as he could with the van. She asked would he like to come in for a cuppa and a slice of toast before he went.

'Regretfully, I'll have to refuse your offer,' he said. 'I'll have to put my foot down and get to the docks to catch my mate, but you can fill me in on everything on the way to Liverpool.'

She thanked him once again and watched him climb into his vehicle, waved and shut the door and returned to Milly to tell her what Kyle had proposed.

'I told you he was a good man,' said Milly.

Probably too nice for his own good, thought Jane, deciding to pay him something whether he liked it or not. During these difficult times, a man couldn't afford to sell himself too cheap. For all he knew he might get laid off unexpectedly, so he needed to have money behind him to pay the rent and feed himself.

He returned within an hour and set about loading all of the furniture and boxes into the van. Jane was pleased to see Milly pull her weight; the girl was ferrying boxes in and out of the house quickly and efficiently. The three of them struggled with the larger items such as the wardrobe, but Kyle roped in a burly passer-by to help them and Jane gave the man half a crown for his assistance.

Once they were all packed up and ready to go, Jane looked back at her home for so many years with a pang. She might be back one day, but for now she was looking for a new start but not without remembering the love and kindness she had shared with her loving mother, Lil.

Once in the van driving towards Liverpool, Jane thought it was a good moment to bring up the subject of Milly's wish to train as a typist. Kyle wasn't a blood relation of the girl, but he was almost like her big brother and he might have some ideas about how this could be achieved.

She was thinking of something Andrew had told her about when he was a cub reporter for the *Liverpool Echo*, and he'd been given the task of researching the growth of Liverpool and its docks during Victorian times.

'It had come to light that not all the labourers who had flooded into the expanding port seeking work over the years were uneducated.' She told Kyle as the three of them sat high up in the front cabin of the big lorry. 'Some of the men had come down in the world and had to take any job available to support themselves, their wives and their families.'

'What has all this to do with our Milly?' Kyle asked her.

'Well, sometimes the wife was educated as well but had to come down a peg or two as well. I'm wondering if there might possibly be a woman who would welcome a private teaching job for a few hours a week, either in her own home or even in Milly's grandmother's house.'

'That would be perfect for what I need,' Milly said excitedly.

'Hang on now,' Kyle urged. 'I don't know how much chance we have of finding someone like that, but I'll ask around.'

'If anyone can do it, you can.' Milly grinned at Kyle, who kept his eyes firmly on the road.

The rest of the journey was jolly, but Jane had not reckoned on Kyle's manly pride. Once they had arrived in West Derby Road at the house a few doors up from Marjorie and Gordon, it didn't take them long to unpack the van, with the help of her new neighbours. Once all the heavy furniture was in place, she thanked him and

Gordon and Marjorie for their help and poured them a beer, thinking it had been thirsty work. After Gordon had left, she thrust a ten-shilling note in Kyle's hand. She had given Gordon some money earlier to share with Marjorie for both their assistance in finding her a new home and settling her there. He had been grateful for the money for after all they had three mouths to feed.

Jane felt Kyle's hand clench over hers and she became aware that he seemed determined to press the note back in her hand.

'No,' she gasped. 'You must take it as half of it is for the owner of the vehicle, the other half is for you. After all a labourer is worthy of his hire.'

'But you didn't hire me,' he said as they tussled over the note. 'My labour was a favour to you. I offered my help.'

'I know that,' she said, aware of the strength in his hand. 'But I can afford to pay you. Lil had been thrifty for years as had her elderly aunt before her. They weren't short of a bob or two and they would want me to share it with the people who have helped me.'

'All right, you don't have to rub it in that you're a step above me,' he said, a flush on his cheeks now.

'I'm not doing anything of the sort,' Jane said. Her head was starting to swim, feeling a mixture of guilt and annoyance that he had taken her genuinely-meant gesture so badly. 'It's your masculine pride that's coming between us. Be honest and admit you could find a use for the money. None of us should be so stubborn in these hard times.'

Kyle unclenched his teeth and released his grip on her hand taking the note with it and putting it in his pocket. 'Have it your way,' he said, an arm going around her to keep her upright. 'I'll accept your money. I know a woman who's in desperate straits and I can use it to help her.'

Instantly, Jane wanted to know who the woman was but determined not to grant him the satisfaction of asking. Instead, she said, 'The money is yours to do with as you see fit. Now if you'll excuse me, I've still plenty of work to do here.'

Milly, who had been watching their struggle with interest, considered he released Jane's hand with a certain amount of reluctance and decided that she must do her best to help them make a match of it someday. It was plain as the nose on her face that Kyle had taken a fancy to Jane. But who was this woman he had mentioned? She was going to have to find out; he had such a soft heart that she wouldn't put it past him to have taken a young widow with a couple of kids under his wing to keep them out of the workhouse.

Finding out the truth was going to have to wait as she had work to do right now and there was the bigger task of finding out the truth about her father and a private teacher to teach her to type. She squeezed past Jane and hurried after Kyle.

'Wait,' she said as he unlocked the van. He gazed down at her with a tight smile.

'What is it, Milly?' He sounded vexed.

She stretched up and kissed his cheek. 'You are a love. Enjoy your day.'

'You too,' he said, ducking his head inside the van, closing the door and driving off.

–

Jane and Milly were exhausted by the end of moving day and after a cup of cocoa and a slice of bread and jam, they went to bed. Jane to dream of Kyle holding her tight and Milly of her father scrabbling up from a burrow like a rabbit while she sat under a tree at a desk, typing away. She woke with a start, wondering if the dream was a sign from God that her daddy was alive as Grandma Martin believed. Milly told herself that she must not give up hope or allow her desire to learn a skill and get a job distract her from finding him.

She went downstairs and lit the fire and as soon as it had taken and was glowing at its heart, she put the kettle on. It was Saturday today and she was going to go back to her grandmother's and would be staying there from now on; her nomad days at an end for now but she wanted to make Jane her morning tea as they had become accustomed. Jane had ordered a gas cooker and although it had been delivered it had yet to be connected so Milly set a trivet over the fire like her mother had taught her to do in her younger days.

It took longer for the kettle to boil this way, so while Milly was making a pot of tea Jane came downstairs.

Milly fetched more coal for the fire as it had burnt low and she did not want the room getting cold while she was helping Jane with the housework. There was still so much to do, but with the two of them at it they'd be done in no time at all.

'I'm going to see that sister of Andrew and Anne's neighbour who happens to live in Kensington later today.'

'What's the sister's name?' asked Milly.

'I think it's Cathy Cain, who still lives up here with her son. The sister down south is called Sally.'

'I remember now,' said Milly. 'They both married soldiers and Cathy's was killed in the war. Sally's husband is a cockney and they met down south. He survived the war.'

'At least Cathy has her son, a little bit of her husband which must make her feel he's not completely lost to her,' Jane said with a sigh.

'I wonder how old the son is and whether he looks like his father,' mused Milly.

'We'll probably soon find out as she's bound to have photos of both,' Jane said.

–

After they had washed and dressed, they headed out towards Kensington. It was now December and Milly could feel the winter starting to bite. As they arrived at Cathy's house, the woman was closing the front door behind her and was dressed for the outdoors. Jane introduced herself and Milly, and explained who they were and why they had come.

Cathy was short and looked a little under-nourished, the checked woollen coat she wore hung on her small frame, and her face was pinched with hollows beneath her sharp cheekbones. She said in a whiny voice, 'It's nice to meet anyone who knows Andrew and Anne, they're a lovely couple and so in love. I was just off to the shops in Prescot Road, but I can spare a few minutes if you'd like to come in and have a cup of tea, so you haven't had a completely wasted journey.'

They went inside and into a back room that overlooked a yard. 'This house is only small but it's home,' said Cathy. 'Me and me fella moved in here in 1910 the year the old king died. He wanted to volunteer straight off when war broke out in '14, but I put me foot down. Still, he had to go eventually, but I was able to carry on working for a while and I have me Jimmy to look after me now.'

Milly thought she said this in a very doleful way as if she was an old woman, but she was only around the same age as Marjorie. 'What job did your husband have before he was a soldier?' she asked.

Cathy did not answer, saying, 'I learnt to dress and cut hair, me mother was a hairdresser.' She fussed around getting out cups, milk, sugar and warming the teapot. 'It won't make me rich, but at least it's brought in some money after me fella was killed. After he was gone I received my widow's war pension which meant I could support meself and me boy as he grew up. After the war I found myself a job cleaning at a school in Chatsworth Street. I'm still there and I do the hair of the local women who can't afford fancy salons in their homes.'

'That's a piece of luck, we were talking about Milly having a new hairdo, weren't we?' said Jane.

'I'd like to have fashionable waves like Jane's,' Milly concurred.

'Yes, I can do that, why don't you come over one day, and I'll do them for you. It's three shillings with the chemicals included.'

Milly thought of her dwindling coffers and said she'd have to think about it. 'What does your son do?'

'Jimmy's an apprentice joiner.' She picked up a couple of framed photos and held them out to Jane.

She showed them to Milly, and they exchanged glances. Milly immediately recognised him as the young man who was with Liam and Franny at the O'Donnells' house.

'Your son has a look of your husband,' Jane said.

'Yeah, and he has his gentle manner, although he can be tough when he needs to be,' said Cathy. 'Anyway, he's good at woodwork, so an old mate of his father has offered him an apprenticeship. He's a joiner himself by trade, but he's still suffering from gas inhalation effects from the Great War. He needs help but can't afford to pay a journeyman's full wage, though can manage an apprentice's wages. Jimmy is strong and good with his hands, so will be a real help to him. We don't have much money.'

'Is Jimmy at work now?' asked Milly.

Cathy nodded. 'Oh yes. Six days a week and the only day off is the Sabbath. His wages will be a help to us, however small. Our Sal has offered to pay both of our fares down to Southend for Christmas which I appreciate more than ever.'

'You have a generous sister,' said Jane.

'As she says family should take care of their own… and she's still got her man.' She could not conceal the envy in her voice.

'What about your husband's family, do they give you any help?' Jane asked. Then adding, 'I shouldn't be asking, I suppose, but you've been so forthcoming about your situation that you've roused my interest.'

'No, they are no use, but we are getting by.'

Milly said, 'And it wouldn't surprise me if you know a fair amount about us.'

Cathy agreed that she did know something of their stories, such as Jane being Andrew's sister whom he believed had died at birth. Also, how Andrew had saved Milly's mother from drowning in the Mersey. She paused. 'He told Sal that you and your mother had gone to Ireland to stay with family there. Is your mam well now?'

Milly thought she detected a touch of spite in the woman's voice. 'She's still in Ireland and she's grand. She loves being part of a large family, but I felt smothered. I couldn't move without them wanting to know what I was doing or where I was going. Besides, I missed Liverpool, so I've come back. I'm almost fifteen and hopefully I'll be able to find some paid work.'

'There are families that can't stand the sight of each other. It was like that with me fella and his brothers, all except for one. Now his niece has turned up. She's been thrown out by her mother for being too much of a handful and is staying with us for a while, but she's more trouble than she's worth. I worry about her leading my Jimmy astray, he's such a gentle soul.'

Milly wondered how Jimmy felt about his mother being worried about his moral well-being. She thought this woman would be stifling to live with and reminded her of her Irish aunts and her grandmother. Suddenly there came a loud booming noise that caused Milly to jump to her feet.

'We've kept you too long if you wanted to do your shopping before the shops close for lunch,' she said. 'That was the noon day gun if I'm not mistaken.'

'I still might make it to the butcher's and bakery if I put me skates on,' Cathy said, leading the way to the front door. As they parted, she said, 'Drop by any time you're down this way.'

Jane nodded. 'And you must come and visit us, too.' She gave her the address and directions.

'I know it,' said Cathy. 'Jimmy plays football in the park sometimes and has met up with a boy called Liam from near Scotland Road way.'

'Is his name Liam O'Donnell?' asked Milly.

Cathy nodded.

The wind had risen, so Milly tightened her headscarf as she and Jane went their separate ways, Milly thinking that she hadn't heard the last of Jimmy Cain.

Chapter Eight

It was getting dark by the time Milly arrived back at her grandmother's house in Waterloo, she felt cheered by the warm gas light that drifted through the windows and as Susan bundled her into the house after she had wrung the bell.

'Come inside, Miss Milly, dinner will soon be on the table.'

Milly removed her coat and scarf and hung them on the tall coat stand in the large hallway. She found it strange to have gone from the squalor of the O'Donnells to the comfortable affluence of her grandmother's in such a short space of time. She pinched herself to make sure it was true, but she was still standing there a second later, so told herself it must be real.

'Come in here and see me, Milly,' her grandmother called out from the dining room.

Milly entered the room and was pleased to see a large dining table, covered in a lacy tablecloth with fancy china, silver cutlery and crystal glasses laid out for the evening meal. She was going to be dining like a queen, she thought. Her tummy rumbled and she remembered that she had barely eaten anything except scouse or bread and jam for what seemed like ages.

Her grandmother enquired about how Jane's move had gone, and Milly told her about the breakdown of the removal van and Kyle stepping in.

'I think he likes her, and she likes him,' Milly said.

'Jane is a very pretty and sensible girl, she'd make a wonderful wife, but she is too young,' said Adelaide. 'If Joseph had waited a little longer, he might have found a better wife than your mother.'

Despite Bridget's obvious failings, Milly felt a stab of loyalty for her mother. 'She's not all bad and besides…' Milly looked up as Susan entered the dining room carrying a steaming tray containing a hot pie and a silver server of fresh vegetables. 'You wouldn't have me as a granddaughter if Daddy hadn't met Mammy.'

'That is true,' Adelaide agreed.

Susan served up the hot pie onto both of their plates and Milly helped herself and her grandmother to some vegetables and some of the gravy which Susan had placed on the table in a small pouring jug.

Milly took a bite of the pie, it was beef and suet and was delicious. She couldn't remember eating anything quite so wholesome and tasty in ages.

After their dinner, there were afters of stewed fruit with custard. Milly was a little disappointed as she had half hoped for a spotted dick or a treacle sponge, but beggars couldn't be choosers, she supposed. When they had finished, her grandmother moved to the comfortable parlour where she turned on the wireless and they both listened to Sandy Powell which made them laugh and then it was a promenade concert from Eric Coates and his light orchestra.

Later, upstairs in her room with its heavy damask curtains pulled shut for the night, Milly unpacked her Gladstone bag containing her few belongings and wondered what the future held for her now. She slipped under the crisp cotton sheets covered by a warm, peach-coloured eiderdown and her head was full of her mother and father and the face swimming in front of her eyes as they closed in tiredness, was Jimmy's.

—

Later that week, once she was settled into a routine, Milly told her grandmother that she was going to visit Jane who had called from the telephone box to say that she had the Saturday off and to come over as Kyle was coming to see her too.

When Milly arrived at West Derby Road, Jane told her all about working in the hat shop in the city. 'They have all sorts of hats, Milly. Fancy ones for Ladies' Day at the races, ones with veils for funerals and even turbans for doing the washing or lounging in the bath. You get all sorts of customers. Some are nice and some of them are rude, but Mrs Briscoe, who runs the shop, is very strict and says the customer is always right. Some women take hours to choose a hat.'

'I'm happy with my knitted one,' Milly said.

'You need to shake things up when you get some money. Did you think about taking Cathy Cain up on her offer of doing your waves for you?'

'I can't afford them, yet,' Milly grumbled.

'Why don't you let me make you a loan?' Jane offered.

'That's very kind of you, but I couldn't.' Milly thought Jane had been too nice to her already.

'I insist. A haircut would be just the thing and will give you a lift. Besides, it will give you encouragement to get a job.'

'Never a borrower nor a lender be,' Milly cautioned.

'Don't be silly, it's just a few shillings and I know you are good for it.' Jane opened her purse and handed Milly three shillings.

'You're a pal. Thanks.' Milly felt a sudden excitement wondering if Jimmy would be at home when she called but then remembered he'd have to see her with a towel over her head. 'Maybe I could go tomorrow.'

Soon after Kyle turned up with a letter from a Mrs Rogers who lived in Upper Mann Street in Toxteth. 'I said I'd deliver it for her and save the price of a stamp,' he said. 'She used to be a shorthand typist but had to give up her job when she married.'

'You found someone quickly!' said Milly and Jane in unison.

'One of the fellows at the docks told me about her, she's a friend of his wife, and I had the impression from you it was urgent,' he said, watching as Milly slit open the envelope with a knife.

The letter was brief and to the point and more importantly it was neatly typed. 'What does it say?' asked Jane.

Milly handed the sheet of paper to her. 'Here read it yourself,' she said.

Jane read it and then lifted her eyes to Milly's face. 'She's offering to teach you shorthand as well. She asks can she come to your home around half past nine in the morning and is asking whether she can bring her youngest with her and stay until two when she must leave to be back when the other children come home from school.'

'She doesn't say what payment she wants,' said Milly.

'She wants you to make her an offer,' said Kyle.

'What do you suggest?' Milly asked the two adults.

'Seventeen shillings and sixpence a week would be about right from what she told me she earned a few years ago,' he said. 'I'm going to have to go, ladies. See you soon. Shall I tell her husband she's to come to your grandmother's tomorrow?'

Milly nodded, hoping her grandmother would help her out with a loan to pay Mrs Rogers.

'I'd better be going.' Kyle stood to leave.

'Let me see you out.' Jane followed him out into the corridor and opened the front door for him.

'So, Jane, when am I going to have those tea and scones – just you and me?'

Jane felt herself flush, but she wanted to know something else first. 'That depends on who the destitute woman is that you are helping out so enthusiastically.'

'Maybe you should come round and see for yourself, you have my address.'

'Maybe I'll be too busy. I only get a half-day closing on Thursday and every other Saturday off, except for Sundays.'

'How about your next Saturday off?'

'I'm not making any promises.'

This didn't seem to bother him unduly and he gave her one of his confident smiles. 'I'll look forward to seeing you,' he joked.

She curtly thanked him for his help, and couldn't stop her own smile from spreading across her face, but composed herself before returning to Milly. 'Now, let's think about this Mrs Rogers. The fact that she hasn't pawned her typewriter suggests that the family aren't on their uppers. But I think we should pay for paper and typewriter ribbons as you're going to be using them.'

'What and her shoe leather too if she's going to walk here?' said Milly with a bit of sarcasm. 'Do you think she has her own typewriter or expects us to have one here?'

Jane looked again at the letter. 'It doesn't really say. Perhaps Kyle would give her a lift the first time if she's bringing her baby and a typewriter. Unless she brings the baby in a pram, then she can place the typewriter in the basket underneath the pram.'

'That would make sense,' said Milly. 'Although, what would really make sense is for me to go to her. The fact that she doesn't suggest it could mean she wants to spend some time out of the house,' Milly added. 'You don't think I've acted too hastily, do you?'

'You mean that perhaps we should have interviewed her first or seen where she lives?' said Jane. 'I think we can trust Kyle, but I'd be interested to see the area she comes from. I know so little of Liverpool. It's not too late, maybe we should pay her a visit now?'

Milly agreed, so they had another cup of tea before setting off for Toxteth in south Liverpool, presuming Upper Mann Street would be close to the Mersey as there was an area called Mann Island down that way. As it happened, Upper Mann Street ran horizontally to the river and was several streets up from the docks. It was a street of three-storey houses each with a basement – once upon a time they had probably been the homes of wealthy shipowners who had moved out to more affluent areas as workers moved into the port; most likely several families lived in each house now. They stopped at the house number written on the letter; there were two women standing at the bottom of the steps, leaning on brooms and gossiping while a man sat at the top of the steps, smoking a clay pipe.

Jane asked him if he knew a Mrs Rogers and received a reply in the affirmative. One of the women offered in a singsong Welsh accent to fetch her. Jane thanked her, and she and Milly waited outside while the other woman swept the pavement in front of the house and deposited the rubbish in the gutter. It was a good few minutes before she reappeared with a careworn woman in her thirties. Her face looked as if it had been washed that morning and her clothes were clean if a little threadbare. She carried a babe wrapped in what appeared to be a crocheted handmade shawl in a variety of colours. Milly guessed from its appearance it had been re-made from several used garments that had been unravelled and combined again. The woman gave them the slightest of curtseys which took Milly by surprise.

'You're Mrs Rogers?' said Jane.

'I am,' she replied. 'I wasn't expecting you.'

'No, but we thought we'd pay you a visit,' said Milly.

'May we go inside and discuss matters there?' asked Jane after introducing herself.

Mrs Rogers instantly appeared flustered and said, 'I haven't had time to tidy up or go to the shops, so I haven't anything in to make you a cup of tea.'

'We haven't come for tea and we won't keep you long,' said Milly.

Still, Mrs Rogers hesitated, but eventually she turned and said, 'Follow me.'

Jane and Milly were close on her heels as she led the way upstairs to the second floor and into a large untidy room containing two double beds, a single one, as well as a cot. A coal fire appeared to be on its last legs, and they guessed it would not be lit again until evening despite the cold weather. There was a sash window that reached from floor to ceiling and the curtains were several inches too short, Milly guessing they had come from a previous house. There were no toys to be seen and the only other furniture items were two well-worn easy chairs, a dining table and four dining chairs with scuffed legs. It was clear these were the possession of a family who had been doing well at one time, but who now, were not. On the dining table sat a typewriter.

'My husband, Tom, never thought he'd be living like this when he quit the farm near Wrexham and I certainly had different dreams when I left Coventry with my brother,' Mrs Rogers said.

'What happened?' Jane asked.

'My brother was killed in an accident at the docks. Tom was a foreman who witnessed what happened and, although I had a job in the shipping office and my brother had paid into a death insurance policy, Tom felt sorry for me and fought to get me some compensation as the owners were at fault. Later, we married and were happy when the first two children came along, but the last couple of years have been difficult as the children started coming in twos. The rent went up and so did the cost of food and coal. If we'd had family living in Liverpool, they'd have helped us but as it was, we've just struggled on alone with our seven.' She paused for breath.

'You don't get any help from the dole?' said Jane.

Mrs Rogers shook her head. 'Very little, they pry into everything. The main reason I want to work outside at your home is so they don't get wind of my employment. As it is, they've suggested I pawn or sell my typewriter. I've refused as it was the last present from my parents before they died of the Spanish flu. It's the only thing of value I have.'

Milly felt a strong deal of sympathy for the woman who was clearly of quite good breeding and struggling with coming down a peg or two in life. Milly knew how that felt. She jumped in quickly with the sum she and Jane had agreed to offer Mrs Rogers. She beamed and accepted the offer and promised to be at Milly's grandmother's house at nine-thirty the following Monday morning.

Jane and Milly left after that and discussed Mrs Roger's story most of the way to Waterloo. The mention of the babies coming in twos fascinated them. One set of twins was burden enough on a family's budget, but it sounded as if the Rogers had had more than one set of twins if they had seven children.

When they arrived in Waterloo, they told Adelaide all about Mrs Rogers; she thought that the typing lessons were a great idea. Her attention seemed completely capti-vated by her granddaughter's mention of Mrs Rogers having two sets of twins.

'I had a twin brother, Barnaby, as you know, but sadly he and my father couldn't agree on his future, my brother always wanted a career as a performer on the stage. When he was thirteen, he ran away and it nearly broke my parents' hearts, only they had this conviction that because I was his twin, that I should be able to sense if he was alive or not. They even believed that he would try telepathy to send messages to me – I told them he'd never used telepathy to get in touch, but even so I was convinced he was alive and in Ireland, because one time I met an Irish comedian and singer at the Empire in Liverpool, I can't remember his name, but he told me he had met Barnaby at a show in Ireland. Father was furious with Barnaby leaving home thinking he could make a living making people laugh at his antics. He accused me and

94

Mother of having encouraged Barnaby.' She paused on a sob. 'I was shattered by his accusation and Barnaby's disappearance, despite being convinced he was still alive. I was never the same person afterwards, and when my Joseph went missing too the grief nearly destroyed me.' She fell silent and it was several minutes before she spoke again. 'Bring Mrs Rogers to see me when she comes and ask her to have a photograph of her twins with her. I'd like to talk to her about her twins as well as to see how alike they are. Despite my brother and I being of different sexes, there was a strong similarity between us. Your father was very like my brother, Milly.' She sent for her cash box and handed over thirty pounds to her granddaughter. 'For expenses and to pay Mrs Rogers.'

Her grandmother was tired by the conversation and went for a rest which left Milly and Jane chatting.

'That's the first time Grandma has told me the whole story of her twin's disappearance,' Milly said. 'And I'm thinking I'll need to give Mrs Rogers travelling expenses with her coming all the way to Grandma's. Originally, I was thinking of her just coming to your house.'

'Never mind that for now. We were talking about your grandma. Are you thinking she's getting confused and has made it up?' asked Jane.

'I don't know what to believe,' Milly said.

'How old is your grandmother? If her brother ran away at thirteen there might never have been a photograph.'

'I'm sure I've seen a photograph of her parents and they appeared to be quite young and if Grandma is around sixty that means she and her twin were born around 1870 or so. I'll ask Grandma if she has a photo of Barnaby and herself – not that I can see it being of any help to us in tracing

Daddy,' said Milly. 'Her twin must have left home about 1883 if that's so.'

'Let's go to the library and see if we can discover what was going on then,' suggested Jane.

'Not now if you don't mind,' said Milly. 'I'm tired and hungry and Mrs Rogers will be coming tomorrow. Besides it's getting dark, you should be going.'

—

The next day was a Sunday and Milly took her grandmother to the local protestant church; the service was quicker than the Catholic one in Ireland, although Milly still thought the sermon from the vicar could have been much shorter. Afterwards, she told her grandmother that she was going to have her hair done at Cathy's house in Kensington.

When she arrived, she was pleased to see that Cathy was expecting her because Jane had told her she was coming, and had a seat ready in the kitchen. Next to it were laid out all the necessary tools for the job: a pair of sharp scissors, a bottle of setting lotion and set of curlers as well as a narrow comb to apply them with.

Milly had brought her own towel and after Cathy had washed Milly's hair over the sink with a bottle of Dreen shampoo, she sat her in the chair and set to work.

'Your hair is lovely and long but I won't cut too much of it off, it will bounce up with the curlers,' Cathy told her.

Throughout the process Milly was bombarded with a constant monologue all on the subject of one thing: Cathy's son Jimmy and what a wonderful boy he was.

'Does your Jimmy have a young lady he walks out with?' Milly asked mischievously.

'No, he hasn't any truck with the young girls around here, they're too saucy and common. When he's older he'll find a nice girl at the church we attend.'

Milly felt like laughing, thinking that the Jimmy she had met was more interested in girls than his mother imagined.

'There now,' said Cathy, showing Milly her new hairstyle in the mirror.

Milly loved it and was just admiring the soft waves, when she heard the front door bang and in came Jimmy into the kitchen.

'Hullo, what's this?' he said, not seeming to recognise her. Milly was struck by his shiny dark hair and his lean and fit physique. He was a handsome fella. It was only when she opened her mouth that the penny dropped for him when she said, 'We've met before, at the O'Donnells' house.'

'You're not that cousin, are you? You look all different… and older.' Milly thought he was looking at her in a new way and quite liked it but wasn't sure his mother did.

'What happened to your cousin, Franny?'

'Oh, she's gone back to her father's house. They took her back, she was too much of a handful for Mam.'

'She's not the right sort of girl for Jimmy to be involved with, I'm very particular about who he associates with.' Cathy pursed her thin lips.

Milly saw Cathy give a sideways look in her direction which she caught in the mirror she was holding.

'Isn't it time you were going?' Cathy said, more pointedly. 'That will be three shillings.'

Milly felt in her purse for the money and had barely got it out before she was being handed her coat and shuffled towards the door.

'Bye now,' said Cathy.

'I'll show her to the door, Mam,' Jimmy insisted, and though his mother gave a frown, she didn't try to stop him.

'What about a trip to the flickers,' he asked Milly at the door, looking over his shoulder to make sure his mother couldn't hear.

'I don't think your mammy will let you out,' Milly teased.

'Ah, don't mind her, it's only because she cares about me.'

'Well let me know when she gives you permission and I'll think about it.' Milly flicked her hair and headed off in the direction of the tram home, her fashionable waves bouncing off her shoulders.

–

The following morning, Mrs Rogers arrived almost on the dot being dropped off by Kyle who helped her in with the pram into the big hallway. As Milly had guessed, the typewriter was balanced in the foot of the pram. Rose, the baby, was asleep, so they left her in the pram and went into the parlour where there was a table cleared for the typewriter and two chairs were set in place. Mrs Rogers glanced about her and said, 'What a nice room this is.'

Milly said, 'It catches the sun in the mornings and warms it up, so there's no need for a fire until evening if we want a spot of quiet to read or do a bit of darning or knitting. We have the wireless on a lot too which

Grandma likes – she's resting now, but maybe next time she'll be here to meet you as she'd like to talk to you about twins. Now I'll go and ask Susan to make a cup of tea and then we can get started.'

Mrs Rogers told her that her Christian name was Violet and started by explaining to Milly how the type-writer worked and how she needed to learn, while wearing a blindfold, and showing her where the letters, numbers and punctuation marks were situated on the keyboard. That would enable her to type more quickly, rather than having to watch where she was putting her fingers all the time.

When Susan brought in tea and biscuits, they broke off and Milly told Violet what her grandmother had said about her twin leaving home and not getting in touch and wanting to know if Violet's twins had a special link between them. Violet agreed that her twins seemed to know what the other was thinking and often insisted on wearing the same clothes and the like. She expressed great interest in the subject and was more than willing to meet Milly's grandmother to discuss it with her.

'In those days, of course, people could vanish much easier. Was your grandmother's twin the adventurous type? Had he ever mentioned wanting to see more of this country or even the world?'

Susan and Milly exchanged looks and the latter told the whole story about Barnaby wanting to go on the stage.

Mrs Rogers said, 'A Liverpool lad wanting to be in the entertainment business might want to go to America where a fortune could be made in the entertainment theatres, Vaudeville they call it over there. He could have stowed away on a ship or even signed on as a cabin boy.'

'Surely, he'd need his parents' permission to sign on as a cabin boy and a passport to enter America,' said Milly.

'People sometimes turned a blind eye for free employment, he could have worked his passage,' Violet suggested.

'Does it really matter, when it's my daddy we want to find?' said Milly with a sigh and explained about her father being missing too.

'It matters to your grandmother, by the sounds of it,' Violet said. 'You really have set yourself a difficult task, although if your daddy was a sailor, he might still instinctively have a feeling for ships, and he'll be able to smell the sea and will follow his nose. If only we knew more about how the memory works.'

'Jane's granddad is a doctor,' said Milly. 'But we need him to be a special kind of doctor, who knows about the workings of the brain,' she added.

'True,' said Violet, checking the time from the clock on the mantelshelf. 'And since the war, there are more specialist doctors around. I have a Coventry cousin who was in the trenches and was driven crazy by what he saw and heard – shell-shocked they said. He was a captain and was sent up to a special sanatorium in Scotland.'

'Where in Scotland?' asked Milly. 'I'll ask Jane to get in touch with Andrew and to see if he can find out, because he's part Scots and has visited Scotland.'

'The more knowledge you have the more you might understand what is going on in your father's head, Milly,' said Violet. 'Now I suggest you get on with your typing lesson or you'll never pick it up quickly enough. And while I'm thinking of it. Is it possible for me to have some money towards my fare? With having the pram, I'll have to take the train into town. Although tomorrow, I could leave the pram at home if I leave my typewriter here and take a tram.'

'What about the baby?' asked Milly.

'I'll work something out,' Violet said.

Chapter Nine

Later that evening, Milly spoke to Andrew on the telephone at her grandma's and told him what Violet had said about the special hospital in Scotland. Andrew told her that the place for those officers suffering from shell shock during the war was named Craiglockhart in Edinburgh; he wanted to know her reason for asking and she told him.

Andrew promised to speak to his grandfather, Doctor Fraser, and see if he had any light to shed and had mentioned that Doctor Fraser was currently intending to visit Edinburgh from his home in Northern Ireland. Anne had relatives there, and Andrew and Anne had been considering a visit themselves in the next few days, before their baby was due as it would be hard for them to travel once the child was born. He would arrange time off and would ask his grandfather to meet them in Edinburgh and hopefully they would be able to visit Craiglockhart and discuss Milly's father with some of the doctors.

On hearing this, Milly immediately suggested that perhaps she and Jane should arrange to meet Andrew in Ireland. He quashed the idea at once saying, 'Have you forgotten Jane has a job and can't just take time off when she wants and what about your typing lessons and your plans for Mabel Fletcher College that Jane has mentioned to me when last she phoned?' Milly sighed and thanking him replaced the receiver.

—

The following morning, she decided to go into Liverpool with Violet and visit Jane. Violet had arrived on time without the baby; she'd managed to have someone mind the baby while she was working. As it was Violet stayed longer at the house talking to Milly's grandmother about twins having also brought with her a couple of photographs of her twins.

Eventually, Milly managed to tear Violet away and they made their way into Liverpool where they parted, and Milly caught the tram to Jane's. She had just got in from work and was frying sausages for her evening meal on her new gas stove. She already had the kettle on for a cup of tea, so Milly made the tea while telling her about her phone call to Andrew.

'He's right,' said Jane. 'I can't just take time off to go to Scotland with you and you have to continue with your typing lessons.'

'But time is marching on and we're still no nearer to finding out whether my daddy is alive, and if he is, where to find him.'

Jane placed an arm about Milly's shoulders. 'I know, luv, but we also have to get on with our lives and we must all earn money to pay the bills and to eat. I know you're not penniless now you've found your grandmother, but you must be sensible and not run off on a wild goose chase. I presume he hasn't had much luck discovering who your father's friend was during the war either.'

'Oh. He didn't mention it,' Milly said, looking glum. 'I'd forgotten about it, so perhaps he has as well.'

Jane sighed, 'Sometimes I think it would have been best if your grandmother had kept her feelings to herself and not roped you into all of this.'

'You don't understand…' Milly, was upset. 'You never knew your father.'

'No, and from what I've heard about him I'm glad of it.'

'But I loved my daddy and want to find him alive,' cried Milly.

'He could be dead and it's all wishful thinking on her behalf and yours too,' said Jane. 'Raising your hopes when there's no proof he is still alive. If he was, he could find you easily.'

'I know you think I'd be best dismissing what she believes,' Milly said. 'But I can't… and if you can't accept that then I'll just go home and not waste any more of your precious time.'

'That's just silly! I'm only trying to stop you being hurt later on,' Jane said, removing her arm from about Milly's shoulders.

Milly stood and folded her arms across her chest. 'I think you're just jealous because my daddy's someone to be proud of unlike your own.'

A flush of anger darkened Jane's face, she couldn't believe that Milly would refer to the father she had never known, but who she believed to have been a rogue, in this way.

'Now you're being foolish and unkind.'

'I'm sorry you think that but you're best without me in your life,' said Milly, a break in her voice even as her eyes flashed with angry disappointment. 'I do appreciate your kindness to me but from now on I'm going to stand on my own two feet.' She pulled her coat off the peg on the back of the door and stormed out of the house.

Jane made no attempt to call her back or follow her, convinced Milly would soon have second thoughts and come back to apologise. All the same, this unexpected blow to their friendship had upset her and she couldn't settle on any of her hobbies or chores that evening.

—

Jane had underestimated Milly's stubborn determination. Not only did she not return to apologise that evening, she didn't in the days after either. Milly's brain was filled with hurt and annoyance, not just at Jane, but for her daddy for going missing, her mother for all the troubles that she'd given her and at Uncle Willie for making her feel small and powerless.

The next few days she concentrated on her typewriting and learning Pitman's shorthand. The shorthand took some getting used to and at first seemed to Milly to be just a series of squiggles and dashes. Slowly it started to make sense and her typing was coming along too. She had to memorise with her mind and her fingers where the QWERTY letters were on the typewriter keys, it wasn't easy at all.

The money her grandmother gave her was burning a hole in her pocket and she was keen to see Violet right for the lessons she had given her. She felt restless and told her grandmother that she was going to take a trip see Violet who would be depending on her first week's wage. Despite the rain, she set off on the train to Liverpool's Exchange Station and from there she knew she could walk through the city centre to Violet's where Toxteth met the Liverpool boundary. Her mind was still working over everything that had happened. Angry and fearful that Jane could be right and the search for her father might be a wild goose chase made her feel sick, as did the fact that Jane had not even tried to prevent her from leaving. Instead of going the simplest way down to the dock road and left along the dock road and then up right to Upper Mann Street, so deep in thought was Milly that she was unaware that she was heading in the wrong direction by walking up London Road and then into Prescot Road and to Kensington. It was only when she passed Kensington Library that she realised she was heading for Cathy and Jimmy's house instead of Violet Roger's home. She groaned. Her feet were aching, and the damp had seeped through the cardboard from a cereal packet that she had placed in the sole of her shoe after finding a hole in it. Despite her weariness she was reluctant to retrace her steps. Instead, she decided to carry on, seek shelter there and cadge a cup of tea and hopefully a jam butty, as well.

Fortunately, she remembered the address and went up to the front door and banged on the knocker. She was aware of one of the net curtains lifting, and saw a face peering out. Then the curtain dropped and a few moments later the front door opened, and in the doorway stood Jimmy with his jet-black hair. Milly noticed again how tall and lean he was, and despite herself, she felt an immediate tug of attraction as his dark eyes met hers.

'You again?' he said in well-modulated tones.

'I didn't intend coming here,' she said, 'but perhaps it was meant to be.'

'What do you mean by that? Are you loopy or something?' Milly could see he was teasing her as he looked as pleased to see her as she did him.

'No, I'm not,' she said indignantly. 'Although, it wouldn't be surprising if I was, after all I've been through.'

'Whatever are you going on about?' he said. 'You'd better come in because it's obvious you're soaking wet.'

She thanked him and even accepted his pulling her determinedly through into the house by her coat sleeve. He took her through into the kitchen where a fire burnt in the black-leaded range and sat her down in a chair in front of it. 'We'd better get you out of that wet coat first,' he said, helping her off with it.

She sat back in the chair. 'You're bossy, aren't you?'

'I was just helping you. You can catch a chill sitting in wet clothes.'

'Does that go for wet shoes as well?' she asked, smiling up at him as she slipped off her shoes, showing him the hole in the left one, removing the sodden piece of cardboard as she did. Then she stretched her feet out towards the fire.

'You have to be careful doing that,' he said. 'You could end up with chilblains and they itch like mad.'

'Thanks for the warning,' she said, withdrawing her feet and, curling up on the chair, she tucked her feet beneath her.

'So, where were you going?' he asked, putting on the kettle.

She thought he deserved an honest answer, so she told him the whole story about her Uncle Barnaby going missing and it foreshadowing the disappearance of her father. He listened to her patiently while at the same time holding her wet coat in front of the range to help it dry.

'I suppose you think I'm ungrateful leaving Jane's house the way I did?' she said.

'Well it sounds like you flew of the handle, but I understand how you feel about wanting to believe your grandmother and wanting your father to be alive and find him. I lost my dad in the war and I'd love him to be alive.'

She gazed up into Jimmy's face in the firelight and considered how many children here and in other countries involved in the Great War must have felt the same.

'Daddy should have come home to Liverpool with me and Mammy instead of staying in Ireland. I've never understood why he did. It wasn't his fight.'

'He must have had his reasons – reasons he had to keep quiet about if he's alive. It could be that he knew the story about his Uncle Barnaby and decided to try and find him.'

She nodded. 'So, what do I do? Follow my heart and instincts and do what my grandma wants me to do – or do I give up on the idea that Daddy could still be alive, maybe lost and confused somewhere?'

'The way I see it is that you've only got a couple of leads for both men. One, that someone saw Barnaby on the stage after he went missing and told your grandma about it. Two, that your dad might have had a knock on the head and not know who he is. This sounds like a long shot to me, but that Doctor Fraser sounds like he'd have some ideas about that. Maybe you should meet Andrew and Anne in Edinburgh? If you were to find your father with Doctor Fraser's help, it would be a real scoop for Andrew as a reporter,' Jimmy said.

Milly thought of the money her grandmother had given her. 'My grandma gave me money for my expenses and I think this is the sort of thing she'd want me to use it for, but I must go to Mrs Roger's first and sort things out with her.'

'You said she lived down by the docks. I don't think it's safe for you to go there on your own, it's getting dark and it will be evening soon.'

'But I have to go, and I'm not scared,' she lied.

'Well, you should be, an attractive girl like you will get plenty of attention from all the dockers.'

'Flatterer!'

'I'm being honest. Wait until the morning.'

'No, I might miss her.'

He stood up. 'Then I'm coming with you,' he said.

'Thanks, but I doubt your mam would be happy about that.'

'She won't know until it's too late. She'll be nattering to one of the neighbours she's met in the corner shop.' He put on his overcoat and a checked cap. 'Well, are we going?'

Milly nodded, feeling warm inside. 'You're a real gent.'

He shook his head. 'Mam brought me up to care about those who need help.'

He held out her coat which had dried out somewhat and she wriggled into it and tightened her headscarf. 'Come on then, let's go! Don't forget to leave your mam a note.'

He was already pencilling one and propped it up on the mantelshelf.

They left without more ado and were soon striding out along Prescot Road in the direction of town. She had trouble keeping up with him until he seized her hand and tucked it in the crook of his arm. He seemed to know several shortcuts and before she knew it, they had arrived in Upper Mann Street and she was knocking on the door of the house where the Rogers family lived.

The same man who had been sitting on the step the other day smoking his clay pipe, opened the door. He appeared to recognise her because he shouted Violet's name up the stairs. It was several minutes before she appeared, but when she did, she squealed in disappointment and said, 'Don't tell me you've changed your mind?'

'No,' said Milly, 'but I've had to change my arrangements and I could be away for a little while, so I've brought you—'

Before she could say another word, Jimmy suggested they go somewhere more private. Violet gave him a thoughtful glance and led the way upstairs and took them into her kitchen.

'We have to be careful, Milly,' Jimmy said, once inside the Roger's rooms. People might dob her to the dole if they see her getting money from you.

Milly chided herself for being thoughtless and handed Violet a handful of money, saying, 'Here's this week's pay and another on account and I'll see you when I come back.'

Tears welled in Violet's eyes and she thanked Milly in a husky voice before asking her to excuse her a moment, she returned with a printed copy of the keyboard of a typewriter that she gave to Milly.

'When I see you again,' she said, 'I expect you to have kept up your practise.'

The two hugged, and Milly reminded Violet of her grandmother's interest in her twins.

'Maybe I'll pop in while you're gone,' Violet said.

Then Milly and Jimmy left and set off in the direction of Parliament Street and the site where the new Anglican Cathedral was being constructed on St James Hill.

'Is this another shortcut?' panted Milly.

'You could say that,' he said. 'We'll go along Hope Street, then on to Lime Street to find out the times of the Edinburgh trains and get you a ticket. Do you know where Andrew and his wife are staying in Edinburgh?'

'They'll be staying with her cousin Fiona and her husband, Sandy, who live there.'

'Do you have their telephone number?' he asked Milly.

'I can always ring Andrew when I arrive in Edinburgh.'

'Then you can let them know that you're there. You'll be all right on your own on the train, won't you?'

'Of course! I made it all the way here from Ireland. But thank you for caring.' She beamed up at him.

'Well, my mam and Aunt Sal seem to think a lot of their neighbours, so I think I'm doing the right thing. Besides, I'm interested in the outcome of your search. I'd really like you to find your father alive.'

She was delighted with his encouragement and wished he was going with her to Edinburgh but knew that was too much to expect. Hopefully, though, they would meet again.

After enquiring about the times of trains to Edinburgh that weekend, she bought a ticket and was in the process of bidding Jimmy ta-ra and thanks when they were disturbed by shouts and chanting. Both their heads swivelled round and they saw a crowd of football fans pushing their way through the station barriers. Everton fans, she noticed, recognising the blue and white scarves and bobble hats. She remembered that the O'Donnells supported the Blues and to her horror she spotted three of the brothers as well as Franny. She ducked her head swiftly, praying they had not seen her. She held her breath as she heard the clumping of feet go past as she nipped behind Jimmy, attempting to conceal herself from the O'Donnells' sight.

There was a pause and a female voice she recognised, said, 'Look who's here! It's Jimbo. What are you doing here, Mammy's little boy?'

'That's none of your business, Franny,' replied Jimmy.

'Don't you speak to my girl in that tone,' snapped Liam pushing against Jimmy with a hefty shoulder, almost sending him to the ground.

As it was, he stumbled backwards and fell on Milly, though he managed to scramble to his feet quickly and brought his fists up. 'Back off, you!' he said fiercely, 'or I'll knock your block off.'

Liam sniggered. 'You and whose army?'

'This army!' said Milly, pushing herself forward to face Liam. Swinging her Gladstone bag she caught him in the midriff with it as he aimed a blow at Jimmy. Her action caused Liam's fist to miss its target, so it only grazed the side of Jimmy's jaw.

'Fight, fight, fight!' chanted several voices and a crowd of football supporters gathered around to watch.

If Milly had not been in such a temper she would have been scared as they were surrounded by a group of hostile young people, egging Liam and Jimmy on as they squared up to each other.

A strong male voice waded through the crowd, saying, 'Now, now, that's enough of this, get on your way or I'll call the rozzers on to you.' The voice belonged to the station master and one whiff of the police and the Everton supporters quickly dispersed as fast as they had congregated. Liam and Jimmy were being forced apart and stood eyeballing each other.

'I don't know what this is about,' said the man in uniform. 'But I suggest the two of you shake hands and go your separate ways.'

'You must be joking, officer,' said Liam.

'I'll show you if I'm joking, lad. Any more lip from you and you'll be facing the magistrate in the juvenile court in the morning.'

Liam slanted him a dirty look and then signalled to his brothers and Franny, who were lurking nearby, to head for the exit. The sound of chanting and hurrying feet receded into the distance accompanied by the occasional shouting and hollering.

Milly breathed easier and thanked the officer. He moved off, and she found herself gazing anxiously into Jimmy's slightly battered face.

'So, what do we do now?' she asked. 'They'll be on the lookout for you once you leave the station, even if you use one of the other exits.'

'Yeah, Liam and I have come up against each other in footy games. He's got it in for me ever since Franny got sent home because Mam'd had enough of her.'

'He's trouble,' Milly said. 'I'm sorry I got you involved.'

Jimmy shrugged and glanced up at the station clock. 'You'll be missing your train to Edinburgh if you don't get a move on,' he said, grabbing her hand and urging her to the platform.

They stopped at the ticket barrier. 'I'm not going to Edinburgh until the weekend. I'd best go and catch a tram to Waterloo rather than walk all the way to Exchange Station for the Southport train.'

He smiled. 'My mistake. I'd best be going. I don't want Mam getting in a state.'

'I'm going to worry about you,' she said. 'I wish you could come with me at the weekend.' Impulsively, she kissed his cheek and told him that she admired his brains and his nerve. He smiled and Milly noticed his cheeks turn a little pink and they both left by a different side entrance to Liam and took a different route to London Road where they parted and caught trams to their respective destinations.

Chapter Ten

That night when Milly returned to Waterloo, she told her grandmother that she was planning to go to Edinburgh that weekend. Adelaide seemed to approve as it was the sort of thing that gave her confidence Milly was doing something concrete to find both her brother and her son. Milly left out the bit about Liam and the fight at the station; she was pretty sure her grandmother wouldn't approve of young lassies wielding Gladstone bags at football fans in train stations.

Milly packed her bag again, thinking she was like Thursday's child, always with 'far to go' and promised herself that one day she would check what day of the week she had been born. Before she turned in for the night, she called Anne, who promised to call Fiona in Edinburgh to let her know that Milly was on her way to Edinburgh at the weekend.

–

The journey into Liverpool to make her connection at Lime Street was happily uneventful. But Edinburgh was an awfully long way on a train, though Milly enjoyed the leg of the journey as it travelled through towns like Berwick-upon-Tweed and wondered what life was like for the people who lived there. She was grateful for the beef paste sandwiches that Susan had slipped into her bag along with a slice of fruitcake, both wrapped up in greaseproof paper.

It was a relief when the train pulled into Edinburgh Waverley Station and Milly searched the platform for sight of a face she knew. Andrew spotted her first and hurried towards her along the almost deserted platform. He hugged her and led her outside to catch a tram to Fiona's house where they would meet Anne, Fiona and Sandy. Once they were seated on the tram, Andrew mentioned to her that he would meet his grandfather in a few days and they would go to Craiglockhart.

'I'm so glad Anne decided to come,' Milly said.

'She says not even a baby wriggling in her tummy would keep her from seeing her favourite cousin, Fiona. Who knows when we'll be up next after the baby is born?'

'You must be so excited,' Milly said. 'Do you want a boy or a girl?'

'I don't care,' he said, his eyes shining with pride. 'As long as mother and baby are healthy, I don't mind at all.'

Milly thought it was just like Andrew to express that sort of sentiment, unlike other men who might be disappointed if their firstborn was a girl.

He changed the subject. 'So, you've been in young Jimmy's company, I hear,' he said. 'Cathy told Sal all about you.'

'Good or bad?' she enquired, knowing that Cathy was likely to be grumbling about her involvement with her precious boy.

Andrew noticed the look on her face. 'Now, now. Cathy is a good woman, if a little over-protective. Who wouldn't be with a husband lost and only one son?'

'Maybe you're right.' Milly nodded. 'He's a good lad, I don't know what I'd have done without him at Lime

Street.' She launched into the tale of what had happened at the station in Liverpool.

He was suitably shocked. 'His mother will have a fit and be even more reluctant to untie the apron strings. Something she should do if she has any sense.'

Milly sighed heavily. 'He has a conscience that's the thing. I bet he wants to be free, but his father's death means he can't just please himself. Families!'

'That's the reason why Anne wants to be here in Edinburgh to see Fiona. They write, but Anne says it's not the same as talking face to face.'

When they arrived at the house, much was made of Milly's appearance and warm hellos and hugs were the order of the day. It had been a long time since Milly had been made to feel so welcome. It was almost like a homecoming.

Over dinner that evening, they talked about Anne expecting her baby and how she was feeling. Milly thought she was blooming, even if she did look a little tired. They also mentioned travelling to Craiglockhart with Doctor Fraser.

'Don't get your hopes up, Milly,' Andrew warned her. 'It will likely come to nothing.'

All the same, when she went to bed, Milly had trouble sleeping as she was so excited at the thought of what lay ahead. She prayed that it would not be a waste of time after all the planning that had gone into the search for her father based solely on her grandmother's conviction that her son was alive. Hopefully, the specialists at Craiglockhart would be able to advise on the possible condition of her father if he was alive and what might have led him to lose his memory. Her thoughts shifted from her father to Jimmy whom she was already missing. She decided that as soon as the opportunity arose, she would write to him, and her grandmother Adelaide.

She also decided to write to Jane to apologise. Jimmy was right, it was just like Jane to urge caution and Milly had over-reacted. Now she was here in Edinburgh, it didn't feel like a wild goose chase any more. She thought again of Liam at the station and not for the first time, felt a mistrust of him. Why did he have it in for her and now for Jimmy? She felt it was only a matter of time before he'd rear his nasty head once more and cause trouble for them.

—

Meanwhile back in Liverpool, Jane was having difficulty sleeping too, eventually she gave up trying and sat up in bed. She couldn't stop herself worrying about Milly. The girl was headstrong but not half as tough as she thought she was, there was no end of trouble she could get herself into. Jane was torn between fretting about the girl while at the same time being annoyed with her. In the morning, she thought that she would go and see Violet and walked to Mann Street in the hope of seeing her and decided that afterwards she would walk down to the Pierhead and watch the ships on the river, after all she wouldn't have put it past Mildred to have got it into her muddled head that she might just catch sight of her father down at the waterfront.

Jane ran into Violet Rogers at the junction of Hill Street and Upper Mann Street and naturally they fell into a conversation which left Jane with mixed emotions.

'Milly told me that she had to go away for a while and gave me two weeks' wages.'

Violet informed her. 'I presume Kyle is unaware that Milly has gone off,' she said.

'Where on earth might she have gone?' Jane asked aloud, thinking how impetuous the girl was.

'Kyle *might* know,' Violet suggested.

Jane considered it possible that she might catch sight of Kyle down on the dock road, so, she said a quick, 'See you!' to Violet and hurried in the direction of the Mersey. She soon realised she was going to have her work cut out catching sight of Kyle's van through the smell of fumes, and horse manure, and the sound of horns, shouts, engines and the neighing of horses which was enough to make her head ache. She realised now why the *Echo* was always going on about how the sooner the tunnel under the Mersey to Birkenhead was completed, the better life would be.

She had been standing near the old Customs House when she heard her name being called and gazed about her, spotting Kyle with his head out of the van window, waving frantically to her. Taking her life in her hands she managed to dodge between the traffic and arrived at the side of his vehicle in one piece.

'Go to the other side and climb in,' he ordered.

She wasted no time doing what he said and climbed up into the passenger seat. 'I never realised it was still so busy along here what with the slump affecting trade.'

'Yeah, but most of us with work that brings us here would prefer it being even busier. Even with the construction work on the tunnel, it's not the hive of industry it was before the Depression. I look forward to the tunnel beneath the Mersey being completed.'

'Where will the entrance be? Do you know?'

'The *Echo* showed a plan that indicates a main entrance near St John's Gardens, with another exit along the dock road to the north of the Pierhead. It probably won't be completed on time though, due to lack of funds.' He paused. 'So, what are you doing down here – looking for Milly?'

'So, you must know she stormed out of my house a few nights ago, then.' Jane said in a tight voice. 'I thought I'd best let Violet know that Milly has left. I never thought she'd let Violet know herself before she told me. In fact, I did think she might have gone to your house afterwards.'

'If she had I'd have returned her to you and told her to say sorry,' he said. 'You have to remember the poor kid hasn't had the easiest of lives and now when she has people who care about her, the grandmother has her all confused about what's truth and what isn't—' His voice broke off as he gripped the steering wheel and made a sharp manoeuvre. Jane clutched the edge of her seat and prayed fervently as he steered the van through a gap in the traffic and into James Street. After a few moments, she opened her eyes and saw that they were passing the Victoria Monument into Lord Street.

'It's all wishful thinking,' Jane shook her head.

'I lost my father in the war, so I understand how she feels,' he said sympathetically and Jane remembered this kind side to him again.

'So, what next?' she asked.

He shrugged. 'Alright, if I drop you off here? I've work to do.'

'Of course, I'm sorry.'

'No need to be sorry,' he said, 'If you're home this evening, is it all right if I drop by?'

'Why not, I'd appreciate the company.'

He smiled. 'So, will I – I'll just pop in and tell May I'm going out this evening.'

Before she could ask who May was, he drove off and Jane pondered for most of the day on who this May person could be. By what he had said, it sounded as if he saw quite a bit of her. This made her feel disgruntled and caused her to determine not to get too fond of him, although deep within her, she knew that she was already attracted to him in such a way that it would hurt if she was to see him paired up with someone else.

She decided instead of moping for the rest of the day that she would pop in and see Marjorie and tell her about Milly, only to her surprise Marjorie already knew where Milly had gone: Anne had phoned her brother's boss and informed Gordon that Milly was with Anne and Andrew in Scotland. Word had travelled on the family grapevine from Edinburgh that Milly was staying with the couple at Fiona and Sandy's house there.

Jane asked whether Marjorie had shared the news about Milly with Cathy.

'Why do you ask?'

'Because apparently her niece, Franny, is friendly with one of the O'Donnell cousins and it would be better if they didn't know Milly's plans.'

Marjorie said, 'I don't know what you're worrying about. It's hardly likely that they'd trace her to Edinburgh, and why are you concerned?'

'We don't want the O'Donnells in Ireland knowing about her having gone to Scotland and about her belief that her father could still be alive, although perhaps they already suspect that.'

'What d'you take me for?' demanded Marjorie. 'A gossip?'

'We all like to talk and Milly's story is an interesting one,' said Jane, flushing. 'I can't help thinking the O'Donnells' interest in Milly has to do with money. As far as I know she's her grandmother's only blood relative who's still alive. Milly's mother and the O'Donnells must know that and will want to have her back with them to get their hands on her inheritance when the old woman dies, it could be why Bridget is pushing to have Milly's father declared dead. If he is alive as the old woman believes, that'll change matters.' Jane paced the floor.

'It would help if we knew what kind of man Milly's father is or was,' Marjorie said.

'We can't go by what Milly and her grandmother say because they obviously loved the bones of him,' Jane said. 'We need to talk to someone who didn't regard him through rose-tinted glasses.'

'He was a sailor, wasn't he?' said Marjorie. 'The grandmother just might remember the name of his ship.'

Jane nodded. 'We've discussed asking her but as far as I know Milly hasn't done so. I suppose it's also possible he might have done service on more than one ship during the Great War,' she said.

'True. It might be worth your while visiting the Sailors' Home in Canning Place,' Marjorie suggested.

'Where's that?'

'Near the Customs House down by the docks. Someone might remember him.'

'We'd need a photograph. Perhaps we could get one from Adelaide,' Jane said with a sigh. 'Oh, this is hopeless.'

'Stop worrying and leave matters to Andrew. Milly obviously has faith in him so why shouldn't you?'

'Because, despite the way she behaved, I like the kid and don't want her hurt.' Jane made for the door. 'Anyway,

I'm going to visit her grandmother, so I'd better be off as Kyle's dropping by this evening.'

Marjorie saw her out and told her to watch herself on the slippery pavement.

Jane rolled her eyes, thinking, I'm not an idiot but only because Marjorie had rubbed her up the wrong way. Even so, she trod carefully and was relieved when she reached West Derby Road where the sun had melted the frost and the traffic had done the rest on the main road, so she managed to cross to the tram lines without misadventure. Soon, she was seated on a tram going down into London Road where she got off and walked to St Anne Street changing on to another one which took her to Waterloo.

The front door was opened to her by Susan the house-keeper. 'The mistress is expecting you,' she said.

Jane was taken aback. 'You surprise me, I hadn't made up my mind to come until a short time ago.'

'She received a letter at lunch time from Miss Milly which said that you'd probably call and see her. She's cock-a-hoop because she's already had a visitor in Violet Rogers who brought her baby along with her and they've been chatting away about twins. Then we had another visitor who the less said about the better,' said Susan.

'Was she an O'Donnell by any chance?' Jane asked.

'Her mother was an O'Donnell, but she's an O'Connor, very pretty with a lovely voice but pushy. I told her the mistress wouldn't want to speak to her. She looked upset and tried to force her way past me, but I managed to shut the door on her.'

'I wonder what she wanted,' wondered Jane. 'As it is, I suppose we can guess. Anyway, can I come in?'

Susan flung the door wide and ushered Jane inside, slamming the door shut before leading her towards the sitting room and announcing her arrival.

'Come in, dear,' said Adelaide. 'It's quite my day today. That charming woman was here earlier with her sweet baby and we had a talk about twins. She has two lots of them, would you believe? Imagine the work involved. One set is identical boys and the other set are girls, but they aren't. The identical ones do seem to sense what the other is thinking and know what the other is feeling if they have hurt themselves; they finish each other's sentences.'

'But the girls don't?' Jane said.

'Exactly not. I wonder why that is?'

Jane shrugged. 'Maybe one day medical science will find out. In the meantime, did you find the answer you wanted?'

'No, but I've received a letter from my Milly who is in Edinburgh with that nice Anne and her husband, Andrew. He's going to help her find my son.'

'If anyone can get to the bottom of it, it's Andrew,' Jane said.

'You know him well?'

'He's my brother,' Jane told her. 'We were reunited some years ago after many years apart.' She decided not to go into details in case she confused the old lady – that was a story for another time.

The next moment the door opened, and Susan appeared, carrying a tray of tea things. She placed it on an occasional table and poured the tea into two china cups. On a plate were four, iced, fairy cakes.

Adelaide and Jane talked over tea. 'Do you have any memory of any of the ships that your son sailed on?' Jane asked her.

Adelaide appeared to Jane to be staring off to some distant point in the past. 'It was so long ago, my dear, and my mind is not what it used to be.' She pointed to a bureau in the corner of the parlour and told Jane to fetch a small photograph from one of its drawers. There were lots of old papers in the drawer and some other photographs too, but it didn't take Jane long to find the one Adelaide had described as it was near the top of the pile.

She brought it over and Adelaide placed her horn-rimmed glasses on her nose, pointing at the image of a young man. 'That is my son, Joseph. It was taken during the Great War and that was one of his ships in the background.'

Jane peered at the photograph. There was certainly a look of Milly about the fellow, in the determined jut of his chin and in the mischievous twinkle in his eyes. Jane liked the look of him. Second officer Joseph was dressed in the uniform of the Merchant Navy and in the background, Jane could just make out the name of a ship which was HMS *Mamora*.

'This is all I can tell you about his ship, I know none of the names of the others now.' Adelaide shook her head. 'Such a brave boy.'

Jane could see that the woman was becoming melancholy and shortly after Jane excused herself, saying she was expecting a visitor that evening.

Happily, when she arrived home, she found a letter waiting for her from Milly who apologised profusely for her bad manners before going on to tell her all that had happened to her after she had left the previous weekend. Her mention of the O'Donnells at Lime Street station caused Jane to wonder again about whether they could be trusted.

She was glad that Milly had admitted she was in the wrong. It would have irked her if she hadn't apologised but now she dismissed the whole business from her thoughts and had a wash-down before putting on clean clothes that included her favourite Eau-de-Nil jumper and olive-green pleated skirt. Then she brushed her hair until it shone and left it loose, letting the waves swirl on her shoulders, having decided to let it grow, now the shorter bob was going out of fashion.

A rat-a-tat of the knocker signalled the arrival of her visitor. She dabbed a few drops of Evening in Paris perfume behind her ears and went to open the front door.

She recognised Kyle and by the light of the streetlamp she saw he was looking the smartest she had ever seen him in a navy-blue jacket with grey trousers and pale-blue shirt and tie. He was not alone but had a girl with him whom he held by the arm. Jane's heart sank.

'Hello, Kyle,' she said. 'I'm glad you're on time but I wasn't expecting you to bring your friend May with you.'

'She's not May,' he said, giving the girl a small nudge. 'Tell Miss Fraser who you are?'

'I'm Siobhan O'Connor, I've been living with the O'Donnell family and I followed you from the house in Waterloo, Miss Fraser, hoping you'd lead me to Milly.'

'She was hanging around outside here, so I thought you needed to know,' said Kyle.

'I suppose you'd better bring her in,' Jane said.

She invited them both to sit down and put the kettle on. She waited until the three of them had a cup of tea before saying, 'Well, miss, what is it you want from Milly? From what I've heard she has no reason to trust the O'Donnells.'

The girl sighed. 'I'm not interested in what she might have coming to her when her grandmother dies. I'm not one of them. I'm a cousin, my father is an entertainer and I want to find him. Trouble is that he travels all over the British Isles performing. My mother decided it wasn't the right kind of life for a child, so she and I stayed with the O'Donnells, although it wasn't what my father wanted and they quarrelled over it. Now she's since died of pneumonia, I heard, and I think he doesn't know about her being dead.' The girl had a look of such sadness about her that Jane's heart went out to her. 'Milly was looking for her father and I hoped she might be able to help me find mine, because I must tell him about Mammy. His name is Mick O'Connor. He's a comedian and he also he has a good baritone voice.'

Kyle said, 'Perhaps he's gone to America like Charlie Chaplin.'

'Don't say that,' Siobhan said. 'I'll never be able to find him.'

'When was the last you heard of him? You could advertise in a newspaper,' Jane suggested. 'And my brother could probably help there as he's a newspaper reporter.'

'How do I get in touch with him?' asked Siobhan.

'Leave that to me,' Jane said. 'I'll see to it. Now it's time for you to leave, Siobhan.'

'It's dark and I'm frightened,' she said. 'Besides, I don't want to go back to the O'Donnells place. I like Mary but Uncle Brendon drinks too much and Liam isn't nice.' She toyed with a loose button on her coat.

Kyle and Jane exchanged glances, both feeling very sorry for the girl who needed help. Eventually he said, 'May would take her in. She gets lonely and could do with a young 'un about the place.'

'How old is May?' Jane asked.

'She was a friend of my mother's, so she's a good age now,' said Kyle. 'And as it happens, she used to tread the boards, so she might be of some help to Siobhan. I could take her to May's tonight because she lives in the same street as me.'

Siobhan's heart-shaped face brightened. 'That sounds good to me,' she said. 'I feel that I can trust you both.'

'One thing,' said Jane, 'how did you trace Milly's grandmother's new address?'

'Mary knew roughly where the old one was so I asked a neighbour did she know where she had moved to. I didn't mention the O'Donnell's name and I promise I never told any of them.'

Her answer was good enough for Jane, so she asked no more questions and was about to say goodnight to Kyle and Siobhan, when Kyle added that Jane should visit him tomorrow evening instead and she agreed. She shut the door, disappointed that her evening with Kyle had come to nothing and wondering what all this business with Siobhan O'Connor would add to the current mystery.

Chapter Eleven

The following day was a Sunday and as she changed to visit Kyle, she thought how Andrew and Kyle were men who cared about people, unlike some.

Kyle's home was situated a short distance from Stanley Park, according to the map he had drawn, and he had helpfully written the names of streets, roads and landmarks on it due to her being a stranger in Liverpool. She took a tram to Anfield football ground and walked the rest of the way. When she arrived in front of the house it was to find Kyle mending a puncture. The bicycle was a lady's one and appeared to be of some age.

When Jane's shadow fell on him, he looked up. 'I won't be long,' he said. 'I'm just fixing this up for Siobhan.' Before she could ask why, he changed the subject. 'So, what did Andrew have to say?'

'He's going to ask a few journalist friends who write about the entertainment world to see if they have any word regarding where Mick O'Connor might be. Some are getting on and will be familiar with names from the past. Milly also put a good word in for the girl.' Jane glanced up at the house. 'Where is Siobhan? Indoors?'

'She's at May's two doors up. She's already been to early Mass and is now helping May prepare Sunday lunch which I'm invited to. No doubt, you'll be welcome too.'

'I had the impression that May wasn't well off,' said Jane.

'She isn't, that's why I've contributed to the cost of the meal despite her saying she doesn't like taking my money. I keep telling her she's doing me a favour by cooking for me.' He was inserting the inner tube into the tyre while he was talking and then reached for a bicycle pump and set about pumping up the inner tube. Then he waited a while before feeling the tyre and fastening the wheel back on the bike. 'This belonged to my aunt,' he said. 'She and Dad were twins, so when he was killed in the war, she fell to pieces and did no more cycling.'

'Is she still alive?' Jane asked.

He shook his head.

'Shame. Milly's grandmother would have enjoyed talking with her about being a twin, it's her obsession.' Jane leaned against the gate post. 'Why does Siobhan need a bicycle?'

'I thought it would save her time getting around.'

'Have you checked whether she can ride a bike? I can't. Lil couldn't afford one and she considered them dangerous.'

'If Siobhan can't cycle, it's not that difficult to get the hang of,' he said. 'It's just a matter of balance.'

'I'll take your word for it,' Jane said, smiling.

'No need to do that,' he said. 'You can have a go before I hand it over to Siobhan.'

'No thanks,' she said, backing away.

'Don't be a coward,' Kyle said, laughing at her dubious expression. 'I'll give you a lift up onto the saddle and then a push off.'

It sounded scary, she thought, but she wasn't going to let him get away with calling her a coward. 'All right,' she said. 'I don't want to be wondering for the rest of my life what I missed.'

He rested the bike against the garden wall and slipped his arm around Jane's waist and then steadied the bike with a hand on the handlebars before lifting her onto the saddle. She felt a thrill shoot through her when his hand didn't let go of her waist immediately.

'Make yourself comfortable,' he said.

She placed a hand on his shoulder and wriggled on the saddle until she was comfortable, aware of the warmth of his breath on her cheek and the strength in the arm around her. She felt her heartbeat quicken.

'Now take your hand from my shoulder and place both hands on the handlebars.' His arm was still about her waist, holding her firmly while setting the bike in motion with his other hand on the handlebars. She clutched his shoulder with one hand and a tiny scream escaped her. He drew away from her and pushed the bike by holding on to the rear of the saddle. 'Peddle and steer with the handlebars,' he said.

'Don't let go of me!' she cried.

But he did, even as he ran alongside her, ordering her to keep peddling. She did so, only slowing down when she neared the main road. Kyle took control of the bicycle and brought it to a halt. They were both laughing their heads off.

'You did well,' he said. 'With a bit of practise, we could go for a ride to Otterspool and have a picnic.'

'A picnic at this time of year!' Jane exclaimed. 'Where's Otterspool?'

'Along the Mersey, south Liverpool. What d'you say?'

'Let's wait until spring arrives,' she replied. 'That's enough cycling for one day!'

'Spring is months away,' he said.

'Exactly, the weather should be warmer and sunnier then. Ideal for a picnic.' She gazed into his face, her eyes dancing. 'I could be a proficient cyclist by then. I'll need to buy suitable clothes, a pair of slacks like the modern ladies.'

'No!' exclaimed Kyle. 'I don't like trousers on a woman.'

'But they're sensible for cycling,' she protested. 'Don't be old-fashioned.'

'You can wear culottes,' he said.

Jane knew they would serve her just as well, so she agreed. 'Don't think I won't wear slacks if I want to, though.'

His eyes flashed. 'We'll see about that! But right now, we'd best make a move back to the house. The food will be on the table. Settle yourself on the saddle and I'll give you a push off.'

With a hint of trepidation Jane did as she was told, and it was a short while before she realised that she was cycling with only the slightest wobble, unaided by Kyle. She felt pleased with herself despite needing his help to slow down and come to a halt without falling off. Her cheeks were flushed, and her eyes shone. 'I could really get to enjoy cycling,' she said with a hint of breathlessness.

'Good, and if you buy a bike, it'll save you on fares to work and is quicker than walking.'

There was still no sign of Siobhan outside, so they went inside May's house. Kyle propped the bicycle against the wall in the lobby and Jane followed him through into the kitchen.

Sitting in front of the fire on a rocking chair was an old woman dressed in the style of Edwardian times. Her long skirts brushed the floor as she pushed herself up out of the chair which rocked as she did so. Despite being indoors, she wore a large hat with what looked like ostrich feathers past their best attached to the brim. Jane thought she was quite the eccentric and smiled to herself that she should have been in any way jealous of her.

'This is Auntie May,' introduced Kyle.

'You didn't tell me she was related to you?' said Jane.

'I'm not his aunt by blood, duckie,' said May. 'It's an honorary title. I was a friend of his aunt and when we got the news she had died, I took on her role. Tea all round?' She bustled over to the two-ring gas cooker in a far corner of the room.

Kyle hurried after her. 'I'll make it, Auntie May. You show Jane the kittens. She might have one.'

Jane slanted him a glance that said, '...this is the first I've heard of kittens.'

May said, 'Is she kind to animals?'

'Would I bring you someone who'd mistreat animals?'

May's wrinkled brow corrugated even more. 'No, but she might be a dog person and not like cats.'

'I do like cats,' Jane said. 'And I could do with a pet to love and keep me company.'

May said to Siobhan, 'You show the lady my pretties.'

Siobhan held out a hand to Jane. 'Come on, you'll be spoilt for choice because they're all gorgeous.'

Siobhan led her over to a sagging sofa, behind which was a large cardboard box lined with an old piece of blanket, in which lay snuggled up the perfectly black mother cat and her litter of kittens.

Jane laughed. 'You're not a witch, are you, Auntie May?'

The old woman glanced up at her and said, 'It doesn't take magic, lass, for my Sooty to produce such a litter. My Sooty might be pure black but none of the kittens are...' she paused, '...now, which kitty, do you want? They have been weaned, although they'll still suckle if she allows it.'

Siobhan was the first to spot one with little white mittens at the end of its paws which she called White Tip, and lifted the kitten out of the box, not without a small amount of protesting and mewling from it. She stroked the kitten gently and brushed her chin against its fur.

May looked for a small cardboard box but after a fruitless search, Jane said that she would carry the kitten inside her coat when she left. Then they all sat down at the table and ate a Yorkshire pudding before the main meal, which came out in a big slab that May cut into slices for them and covered in gravy. Then came slices or roast beef with potatoes, parsnips and carrots. Jane thoroughly enjoyed the meal, not having had a proper Sunday roast for some time. She fed the kitten with small scraps of meat as it lay curled up on her lap. They drank the tea that Kyle had brewed and talked about animals, the weather, people, Christmas, which was on the way, and show business.

May had been a showgirl in music hall and still never missed out on the weekly shows at the Liverpool Empire. It was apparent to Jane that Siobhan had already told May about her father, Mick O'Connor, and her life with the O'Donnells and she was delighted for the girl when May told Siobhan that she had come across him some months back in Llandudno when he had been a stand-in for one of the two baddies in the pantomime, *Babes in the Wood*.

May said that Mick had worked as an odd-job man when there was little theatre work and that he appeared to live in the seaside resort, a permanent resident at a theatrical lodging house where May and some other members of the cast had stayed. 'I'm getting a bit too old now for any of those proper parts, the best hope I have now is to get a part as an old crone!' she cackled. 'It could be that your father is away doing pantomime professionally at this time of year, Siobhan, dear. He could be anywhere – that's the acting life for you.'

'Aren't you upset that he hasn't been in touch with you?' Jane asked. 'I mean Llandudno isn't that far from Liverpool.'

'He doesn't know that I'm still in Liverpool or that Mam's dead,' Siobhan said. 'It's complicated.'

'So, are you going to search for your father just like Milly?' Jane asked.

'I have more clues to my father's possible whereabouts than Milly does.'

'You mean May could give you the name of the lodging house in Llandudno and you could write to him?'

Siobhan sighed. 'I wouldn't know what to say and I'm no good at handwriting. I've missed too much schooling.'

'I could write the letter for you,' Jane offered.

'But what if Dad doesn't want me?' said Siobhan, her voice a sad whisper.

'Is that what the O'Donnells told you?' asked Jane, her eyes flashing with annoyance.

'Mam said it too,' Siobhan admitted quietly. 'She said he had no time for her family, and she wasn't having him criticising them.'

'He's your father, though,' Jane said, 'and he needs to know the situation you're in. Let me write to him if May can give us his address? After all, what can you lose? You could gain a lot. Worth taking a chance, I'd say.'

'Fair enough,' Siobhan said, breathing deeply. 'And I only have to think of Milly and what she's doing to find her father to provide me with hope. I wonder what she's doing now.'

Chapter Twelve

Milly, Anne, Andrew and his grandfather, Doctor Fraser, had settled in at Fiona and Sandy's large Edwardian house in Edinburgh. Milly had really made herself at home. 'I thought I'd do this evening's meal,' she said, wrapped in a pinny as she entered the sitting room. 'I bought some brawn. It's tasty mixed with mashed potatoes, the heat melts it.'

'That's a poor person's meal,' said Fiona, frowning. 'Surely we can do better than that?'

Anne, setting aside the matinee coat she was knitting, said, 'I remember my big sister sending me to Lister's cooked meat shop in Liverpool to buy brawn when I was younger than Milly is now, and we weren't poor.'

Milly thought how brawn had been a cheap alternative from the rice or noodle dishes that her mother often bought when they lived with Mr Chin in Chinatown. Her half-brother Charlie's Chinese grandmother used to dish it up some days when they lived with the old woman and her son.

'You like brawn, I prefer haggis,' said Fiona who had only lived in the Stockbridge area of Edinburgh, which had a village feel to it, since her marriage. Before then she had lived on her uncle's farm, nearer to Glasgow than Edinburgh.

'As much as you like haggis,' commented Anne. 'Brawn was a Saturday lunch, but come evening we had what the men called proper meat – pork chops, steak and the like.'

'All right, you and Milly can have the brawn, then she can go off with Andrew and Doctor Fraser to Craiglockhart. I'll go out later and buy some mutton chops for the men for this evening, presuming Milly, Andrew and his grandfather return from Craiglockhart when they say they will. I can depend on Sandy being in by half past six,' said Fiona, whose facial features bore a likeness to Anne's.

'I'll come with you,' said Anne. 'I could do with some fresh air and exercise.'

'That's fine with me,' Fiona said.

'Make sure you wrap up warmly,' said Milly. 'It's really cold outside. Be careful where you tread, the pavement is slippery in places and the last thing we want is you to fall, Anne.'

'Perhaps Andrew was right, and I should have stayed at home,' mused Anne. 'I really didn't give much thought to it being so much colder up here with the possibility of snow. Fog, I expected, but I didn't realise Edinburgh fogs would be so much darker and denser somehow.'

'It's because the sun doesn't rise as high as it does in England at this time of year,' Fiona said.

'It's very spooky in the evening,' Milly said, shuddering. 'I could imagine those murdering body snatchers way back in the last century lurking in doorways in the Old Town.'

'Burke and Hare,' Fiona said. 'According to Andrew's grandfather most of their victims were people who lodged in the same boarding house as one of them.'

'So, they were murderers, but didn't haunt the streets looking for victims?' asked Milly.

'Worse, they killed many people in the lodging house where the poor fellows thought they were safe. Some of them on their sick beds. A law had already been passed that ensured restrictions on what bodies could be used for medical research,' said Fiona.

'Ugh! Enough of such talk,' Anne said. 'Let's go shopping and be back as soon as possible.'

Despite the fog slowing the pace of their journey, and Anne carefully having to watch her step, they seemed able to find their way to the butcher's without too much difficulty and so it was not long before they were blundering their way back to the house.

–

Much later that afternoon, when the sun had disappeared below the roofs of the houses and night was drawing in, everyone returned to the house and before long, Sandy and Andrew's grandfather were stoking up the fire while Milly took on the task of heating up the kettle on the gas stove; she was thinking about Craiglockhart and the sympathy she had received from the two medical men with whom they had spoken. Their words had given her hope despite them being tinged with caution.

'You're back earlier than we expected,' said Fiona.

'We weren't kept waiting, so we completed our business in no time,' Doctor Fraser, a sparse figure of a man who had kept most of his hair and upright bearing, said in a slight Belfast accent. 'And before you ask, Andrew's gone to have his hair cut.'

'So, did you find out anything useful?' enquired Anne.

'That's what I'm dying to know,' Fiona said.

'We don't want ye to die, so as soon as we've a cup of tea, I'll tell ye what we learnt,' said the old man with a chuckle.

Tea was being poured when Andrew entered the sitting room. His muffler was wrapped high about his neck.

'Feeling the cold a little more now you've been half-scalped?' asked his grandfather.

Andrew nodded. 'The wind has risen and really has an edge to it.'

'At least it'll clear the fog,' Fiona said. 'Anyway, let's have a look at the haircut?'

Andrew unravelled his muffler to reveal a neat back and sides. 'I do feel tidier,' he said, removing his overcoat and hanging it up with his trilby on a hook in the lobby. 'So, have you told the tale yet, Grandpa?'

The old man said, 'I'll get started once you sit down and we've all got our cups of tea.'

Fiona produced a plate of shortbread. 'Dinner won't be ready for a couple of hours,' she said.

They all helped themselves to a couple of homemade biscuits and made themselves comfortable.

'Remember that we have no proof of what has happened to Milly's father, but there are so many examples from the Great War of men getting caught up in explosions. Apparently, it's not that unusual for a man who's been shell-shocked and to have been half-buried by the soil and debris thrown up by an exploding shell or grenade to survive.' Doctor Fraser explained as he stirred his tea.

'One of the doctors who is an expert in the field told us that a man's instinct would be to get as far away from the area as he could and that he may feel compelled to hide out until it was safe to move on,' said Milly.

'Yes,' nodded Doctor Fraser. 'Milly's father's situation could easily have been similar if he was caught up in an ambush with explosives. Both impaired hearing and vision could be affecting him, even years afterwards. It could be that he's lost his memory... It would really help if we knew how he came to be involved in the fighting. After all, as far as we know he didn't have Irish blood.'

Anne nodded. 'He wasn't a soldier in the trenches either, he was a sailor. Isn't that right, Milly?' The girl nodded.

'But there were Irish from the north and south who did fight on the English side during the Great War,' said Andrew. 'Perhaps one of his mates on his ship was Irish and when Milly's father married and went over there, they met up again and that's how he became involved in the fighting.'

'We need to do some more digging,' Milly said. 'Presuming this Irish mate is still alive. We have to find out the name of the ship my father served on during the war and then a list of the crew.'

'The crew could have changed over the years and he could have changed ships,' said Sandy.

'Then we'll have to search the lists throughout the war,' Anne said. 'No doubt Milly's grandmother will have had letters from her son during the war and they'll have the name of the ship on them.'

'Milly will have to search for them,' Andrew said. 'So, what do you suggest we do, Grandpa, in the meantime?'

The old man took a sip of the hot tea before he answered. 'I suggest Milly and I go to Liverpool. I would like to speak to her grandmother, so I can study her mental and emotional state for myself.'

'I'm sorry to put you all to this trouble, but very grateful for your help,' Milly said, sounding embarrassed. 'Also, I can't help thinking, even if he feared for his life, why would my daddy have kept his head down for so long?'

Doctor Fraser said, 'It could be that someone bears him or one of his forebears a grudge. The Celts nurse grudges forever if they're convinced that they or a member of their clan have been wronged.'

'Reminds me of the Orange and Green in Liverpool,' Milly said.

'The McDonalds and the Campbells,' said Sandy.

'There's grudges everywhere, but one has to forgive,' Fiona said. 'One does more harm to oneself by bearing a grudge than to anyone else.'

'But who could my daddy or our ancestors have wronged in Ireland when he'd never set foot there until he married Mammy?'

'Maybe once he married your mother then he was regarded as an enemy by those who had a grudge against her family, as well as for him being an Englishman,' the doctor suggested, thoughtfully.

His words gave Milly much cause for thought herself and she took no more part in the conversation that continued, instead she asked Fiona should she check how the casserole was doing in the oven. She guessed that her grandmother would enjoy talking with Andrew's grandfather, even if she would be impatient and irritable because they were no closer to finding her son.

–

The next morning no time was wasted in setting in motion arrangements for Milly's return journey to

Liverpool and Andrew also telephoned the Adelphi Hotel to make a reservation for his grandfather, who himself put a call through to his housekeeper to inform her that he would not be returning home until in the new year as he was going to Liverpool. He also told her where her Christmas box was and wished her a happy one. Anne helped Milly with her packing while the two men were so occupied, then they all had a huge breakfast with their hosts before Fiona ordered a taxi to take them to Waverley station.

For Milly, it was a bittersweet goodbye. The Frasers and the Andersons had become like a family to her and the time she had spent with them had made her feel like she belonged somewhere again. But her search for her father had only just begun; however, she felt that she was making a little progress now and would have something to tell her grandmother.

'The next time I see you, you'll have a wee baby.' Milly hugged Anne, who embraced her in return.

'You'll have to come and see us in Southend.'

Milly promised her and Andrew that she would and bid them all farewell.

—

It was late afternoon by the time Milly and Doctor Fraser arrived in Liverpool. He had slept for most of the journey. He arranged for a porter to help them with their luggage and told her he would make arrangements to come and see her grandmother in the next few days; Milly picked up her Gladstone bag.

'It's getting on Milly,' said Doctor Fraser. 'Why don't you come with me for afternoon tea at the Adelphi?'

Milly didn't like to take charity but she was starving. Besides, she thought, it would give her the chance to see Jane this afternoon, and tell her that grandfather had arrived in the city.

There was a big Christmas tree in the station and a group of carollers were singing 'Good King Wenceslas'. Milly couldn't believe it was nearly Christmas and that 1930 would soon be ending. She wondered what the next year would bring for all of them.

The hotel was only a short distance away. It was not long before they were told they were in time for tea and that it was being served in the dining room at that moment, she and Doctor Fraser made their way there and indulged their hunger by eating ham and turkey sandwiches, bite-sized sausage rolls and dainty mincemeat tartlets with whorls of cream piped on them, as well as slices of fruit cake.

'That was lovely, thanks,' said Mildred, dabbing away crumbs with an Irish linen napkin. 'Now I'd like to visit Jane, so I'd best make a move and I wouldn't mind a short walk around the shops to see how the shop windows are decorated ready for Christmas.'

Doctor Fraser nodded. 'I'll go and find the bar and have a wee dram and a pipe before dinner and read a newspaper. Tell Jane I'll see her tomorrow.'

Chapter Thirteen

'Guess who?' Milly beamed at Kyle, who opened the door of Jane's house to find her standing there.

'Milly! How nice to see you! You're all we've been able to talk about.'

'Nice to see you too! Although this is a surprise, I was expecting Jane to answer the door.'

Kyle flushed slightly. 'It's Jane's half-day closing at the hat shop and I just popped round to see if she needed anything as I was passing.'

'That's sweet of you,' Milly teased, though Kyle only frowned in her direction and didn't rise to the bait. 'Besides, I thought Jane knew I was coming back to Liverpool,' she added. 'Haven't she and Andrew spoken on the telephone? Anyway, Doctor Fraser decided that he'd like to meet my grandmother.'

'That seems a sensible thing to do,' Kyle said. 'He'll get to the bottom of those visions won't he?'

Milly sighed. 'Are you thinking that as a man of science, he finds it difficult to accept my grandma's visions of seeing my daddy alive?'

Kyle shrugged. 'No, but I can understand him wanting to hear what she has to say first hand.'

'Are you going to leave me standing out here all day?' asked Milly. 'It's cold.'

'Sorry,' Kyle said, 'I wasn't thinking.' He stood aside and ushered her in with a sweep of his arm.

As soon as Milly entered the kitchen she hurried over to Jane and threw herself at her friend. 'Can you ever forgive me?' she said, after a hug, and looking at Jane earnestly.

'Of course, but you had me so worried. Thank God I ran into Violet Rogers who told me where you were, otherwise, I'd have had the law out looking for you.' Jane told her that Violet had also been round to visit Adelaide at her home. 'She's been there at least once and maybe several more. Adelaide seems to have taken a shine to her and those twins of hers.'

Milly accepted an invitation to be seated and plonked herself down on the sofa and proceeded to fill them both in on what had transpired while she was in Edinburgh. 'I've just been explaining to Kyle about your grandfather wishing to speak to my grandmother about Daddy. The doctors at Craiglockhart think it's possible that he could have gone to ground after being caught in the explosion. But we need some more concrete evidence, like one of his old shipmates seeing him, but we don't even know what ship he was on.'

Jane glanced at Kyle and immediately let out an 'Oh!' and she jumped up from her seat. 'I completely forgot to tell you – your grandmother showed me a photograph of your father and in the background was a ship, it was called…' She bit her lip trying to remember while Milly jiggled her leg impatiently. '…I know, it was called the HMS *Mamora*!'

'Now all we have to do is find someone who might remember him,' Milly said excitedly; this was the first proper lead they had received.

'Yes, we could try at the old sailor's home on Canning Place.'

Kyle nodded. 'That's where all those old salty seadogs go to rest when they are retired, the only trouble is the flu epidemic.'

Milly put her hand over her mouth. 'I hope Grandmother is alright, and Violet's children. It's always the young and the old who are in danger.'

'That wasn't the case with the Spanish flu,' Jane told her. 'It was young people such as us, who were more likely to catch their deaths.'

Kyle sighed. 'It's affecting work at the docks, too, with many men off sick. I've been filling in for those men off with the flu. The boss would rather I took time off once they're back, rather than pay me overtime. The general feeling is that the epidemic is running its course, though.' He faced Milly. 'Where is Doctor Fraser?'

Milly's gaze went from one to the other. 'Booked into the Adelphi. I hope you're right about the flu epidemic being nearly over.'

'It's that time of year and they also seem to come in cycles,' said Kyle. 'I've been told to stay away from the orphanage. The thing is to avoid where people gather, such as doctors' waiting rooms, schools, football crowds and always remember to carry a hanky. Doctors are saying that this strain of the flu is not as virulent as some in the past and have advised sufferers not to struggle on with it until the end of the day but to take to their beds and cosset themselves.'

'I've work in the morning,' Jane said. 'I've not been risking taking the tram so far but have been cycling there. It seems miraculous, but out of the three of us working in the shop no one has gone down with the flu yet.'

'I didn't know you could ride a bike, when did you get one?' asked Milly.

Jane stood up. 'Kyle can explain while I make a pot of tea. He's been teaching me.'

Milly turned to him and grinned. 'Oh, have you now! Well, let's hear it?'

He told her the whole story, including Siobhan turning up and what she'd had to say about wanting to find her father.

Milly was flabbergasted. 'I like Siobhan and am glad to hear that she's broken away from the O'Donnells over here. I pray that there's a good chance she'll be united with her father.'

'She's a nice lass and has been good company for May,' Kyle paused. 'So how is Anne?'

'Anne's tired and would like to be home for Christmas,' said Milly. 'I can't wait to see the new baby when it comes.'

'I'm making do with a kitten,' Jane added, placing the tea things on the table. Before taking her seat, the bundle of fur curled up on her lap while she stroked it gently.

Milly's expression softened, and she reached out and touched the kitten's head gently. 'What have you called it and where did you get it from?'

'From May, it's called White Tip, but I like the name Flash, too,' Jane said. 'I'm hoping he'll grow into a good mouser.'

'You've got mice?' said Milly. 'You didn't have them before I left.'

Jane said, 'I'm not overrun with them, but I've seen the odd one and heard a scampering during the night.'

Milly said, 'I saw the odd rat in the O'Donnell cellars when I stayed there, but they kept a dog to catch them.'

'Siobhan is well out of the O'Donnells' house. I don't trust them. Did you know she has a fine singing voice?'

'She does. You've made me think that perhaps I'd better not risk taking the tram to grandma's and picking up germs on the way,' said Milly.

'I could run you and Doctor Fraser there tomorrow,' said Kyle. 'That's if you don't mind a few stops on the way. I suggest you both wear a good size muffler, so you can cover your nose and mouth.'

'Perfect, Milly, then you can stay here the night,' Jane offered. 'We can catch up on all the news.'

Milly nodded and asked if Marjorie and her husband Gordon and nephew Robbie were flu free.

'Robbie caught it a few weeks ago but he's on the mend now,' Jane said. 'Marjorie went down with what was likely just the common cold because she got better very quickly as did Gordon, but it might be wise giving a visit to them a miss this time,' she advised.

Milly sighed but agreed.

Soon after Kyle left, Jane and Milly made ready for bed.

–

The following morning Jane was up first and had brewed a pot of tea before waking Milly. She left for the hat shop, on her bike, shortly before Kyle arrived in his bread van.

'How do you feel about stopping off at the sailor's home and making a few enquiries, we might as well.'

Still tired from all the travelling, Milly had almost nodded off a couple of times, but this idea made her start awake quickly. 'Why didn't I think of that, let's go there now,' she said.

It didn't take long for Kyle to make the detour to Canning Place which was right on the front of the Royal

Albert Dock. At first Kyle wasn't sure if he wanted Milly to come inside with him, telling her it wasn't a very salubrious place for a young woman, but Milly was having none of that. They arrived at the large and majestic building right on the Royal Albert Dock and made their way to the reception area inside.

'No females are allowed beyond the reception area,' said the man at the desk.

'We just want to talk to someone who might know or remember a sailor who went missing some years ago,' Milly enquired.

'The best person for that is Old Jack. He's as old as Methuselah and has a memory like an elephant, never forgetting a face. You can't come inside, young lady, but I'll see if he can come out to talk to you, he'll be reading the shipping news in the library.'

As they sat and waited in the reception area on a bench, Kyle told her that women weren't allowed because of the many 'ladies of the night' who frequented the docks but it wasn't long before a stout old salty sea dog came out to greet them.

'Call me Jack,' he said and sat down next to them. He lit an old-fashioned clay pipe which he had filled up with some Old Holborn rolling tobacco he'd taken from a leather pouch he kept in the pocket of his blue canvas jacket.

With his sailor's cap, Milly thought he looked exactly like the sailor with the beard who appeared on the packets of Player's Navy Cut cigarettes and told him so; he laughed good-naturedly.

'Now what is it I can help you with, lassie?' he asked her.

She told him about her father, Joseph Martin and his disappearance a decade earlier.

Old Jack took a few puffs on his pipe. 'Lassie, I do remember that story of your father and his going missing and I remember him too. I can tell yer now that if he had come back to Liverpool before now and signed on to a ship, someone would know about it. Sailors are a nosey and talkative bunch.'

Milly's heart sank. 'Do you remember anything else about him? Apparently, he was on a ship called the HMS *Mamora*.'

'One thing I can tell you lassie is that he and his friend, whose name was either Tom or Tim, were always together.'

Milly and Kyle thanked the man and when they resumed their journey, Kyle asked her what she thought.

'It sounds to me like Daddy may never have made it home, but then when he disappeared, he may not have been alone.'

Kyle stopped to make a few deliveries before heading for the Adelphi Hotel, parking on Copperas Hill, the road which ran up past the side of the hotel.

Milly and Kyle went inside the hotel and enquired at the reception concerning the whereabouts of Doctor Fraser. The receptionist put a call through to his room and she relayed to Milly and Kyle the message that he would be down shortly.

In no time at all Doctor Fraser made an appearance and after introductions were made, Kyle told the Doctor that he was providing the doctor and Milly with a lift to her grandmother's.

No time was wasted and soon Milly, the doctor and Kyle were on their way to Waterloo. Doctor Fraser already knew about the flu epidemic, having been informed by the receptionist at the hotel and was well-equipped with medication if early symptoms of either that, or the common cold, should make an appearance.

Within the hour they had arrived at Adelaide's house where Kyle dropped them off before tearing away to continue with his deliveries. Susan opened the door to them with a surprised expression.

'I didn't expect to see you so soon, Miss Milly,' she said.

'How is my grandmother, Susan?' she responded. 'I hope this house is flu free.'

Susan smiled. 'So far we've managed to be. We've been having Mrs Martin's groceries delivered and left at the back door. Your grandmother will settle up with them when the danger is past.'

'Sounds sensible,' Milly said. 'Is Grandma up and dressed?'

Susan nodded. 'Up, bathed, dressed and having tea and toasted muffins.'

'Sounds delicious,' said the doctor in an unmistakeable northern Irish accent.

Susan did a double-take. 'You're assisting in the search for the mistress's son, sir?'

'That depends,' said the doctor. 'I'd like to speak to your mistress to see if I can find out a little more about the matter,' he said, smiling kindly.

'So, what name will I give?' asked Susan.

'Doctor Fraser, newly arrived from Edinburgh,' he replied.

Milly could see many other questions hovering on Susan's lips and said swiftly, 'I don't think we should leave Doctor Fraser standing outside in December, Susan.'

Looking flustered by this unexpected turn of events, Susan led them through the house to the morning room. Adelaide glanced in their direction as they entered the room.

'Milly, you have news?' she asked, licking jam and butter from her fingers, gazing at her granddaughter before giving her attention to the man at her side.

Before Susan could announce the doctor, Milly said, 'Grandma, these things take time and before we go any further, Andrew and Jane's grandfather here would like to talk to you. You will gather as soon as he speaks that he is an Irishman which might be helpful in our search for Daddy.'

'I am also a doctor, Mrs Martin, and my grandson has interested me in your son's...' he hesitated before adding, '...disappearance. I would find it useful if you could tell me as much as you can about Joseph and if you have any of his letters that would be of help.'

Adelaide had listened to him without interruption but now she said, 'You're from the north of that country. My dear husband used to go fishing in Armagh. Now what was the lake called... Lough Nay or something like that.'

'You're almost right, Mrs Martin. It's Lough Neagh, your memory serves you well.' He did not wait to be invited to sit down but seated himself on a chair opposite her at the table.

Her expression was calm. 'You wanted me to tell you about my Joseph?'

He nodded. 'Whatever you can remember.'

'I have photos,' she said enthusiastically. 'He was such a handsome boy, just like my brother. One of the girls will know where the big photograph album is.'

'Could it be in Daddy's old bedroom?' Milly asked, wondering aloud. When her grandmother did not reply, she went upstairs and decided to give the room a good search.

It was not until she came across a cardboard box about three inches deep and ten inches by fourteen that she remembered the album had been kept in it along with envelopes containing old birthday cards and certificates. She carried it downstairs and placed it on the table.

'I think this is what you were wanting, Grandmother,' she said.

Adelaide's fingers trembled as she removed the lid of the box and a shaky sigh escaped her lips. It was Milly, though, who removed the large photograph album and turned the first page over to reveal a studio photograph of a couple dressed in the Victorian fashion of the late 1800s.

Doctor Fraser said, 'I'd hazard a guess that this couple are Milly's great-grandparents.'

Adelaide glanced in the direction of the photo and said, 'They are my husband's parents. It was taken in Wales on their honeymoon. The next photo shows my mother-in-law with my husband as a baby.'

The pages continued to be turned showing different stages in the lives of Milly's paternal grandparents, and then her father, Joseph, as a boy, a youth and then a man, until eventually the pages revealed him in his merchant navy uniform with several other men who were obviously sailors. Milly felt this confirmed that he hadn't been in the Royal Navy at all.

'That was his great friend, Timothy,' said Adelaide. 'They had made friends during the Great War.'

She pointed to a young man with a nice smile standing next to her son. Later came several of him and her mother on their wedding day, some group photographs and lastly one of him cradling Milly in the crook of his arm.

'Are there no pictures of your own parents?' said the doctor.

She shook her head. 'My father could not bear to have his likeness taken and would not allow Mother to have hers taken either, nor I and my brother.' She sighed. 'There are a few prints of my twin brother Barnaby and I with my mother that she had taken secretly and then hidden away.' She paused. 'It wasn't until my brother ran away that Father admitted regretting not having a likeness of his son. The police asked for one you see, and it was then Mama came clean.'

'Did he hit the roof?' asked the doctor.

'He was tight-lipped at first and then he thanked her and went straight to the police station with the photograph, knowing it would help in the search for Barnaby.'

'And did it?' asked the doctor.

'The police were able to discover that he had been seen at the Pierhead and from conversations they had with some dockers and sailors, it was believed he could have stowed away on a ship going to the USA.' She paused and took a deep breath.

'And?' prodded the doctor.

'He was never seen at any of the ports there but around about that time two ships collided in fog off the coast of Nova Scotia. The people who dwelt at the port of Halifax along the coast sent out boats to try and rescue as many people as they could, but some died in the freezing waters.'

'A sad story,' said the doctor.

Adelaide tilted her chin and said, 'I believe my brother left the ship before the collision when it called in at

Queenstown, also known as Cobh, in Ireland. I have no physical proof, only a conviction and a vision.'

'Is that because you were twins?' he asked.

'You mean did I have a vision of Barnaby?' she said.

He nodded.

'No, I woke up one night and I had a blinding headache for no reason at all and my right arm ached as well, and several words in a foreign tongue kept repeating themselves in my head.'

'Fascinating,' said the doctor. 'I don't suppose you remember what they sounded like?'

'I wrote the sounds down, but they didn't make any sense to me, so I just placed the paper in my Bible and it's still there.' She hesitated. 'I'll fetch it if you like?'

He nodded.

'Milly, fetch my Bible from the side of my bed.'

Milly rose and did as she was asked. By the time she returned, the doctor had downed a second cup of coffee.

'Any luck?' he asked.

Milly held a black leather-backed Bible aloft. 'It had slipped down the side of the bed. Here you are.' She handed it to Doctor Fraser.

He took the Bible from her and it fell open at a pressed flower and a piece of paper.

'The petals still hold their scent,' Milly said.

He nodded, thinking the paper had certainly been impregnated by the faded petals. He unfolded the paper and read the words her grandmother had written. At first, they made little sense and then he read them aloud with a smile.

'Do you know what they mean?' Adelaide asked.

He nodded, but it was Milly who said, 'It's Gaelic, the old Irish tongue still spoken by some. I don't know what it all means but if this has anything to do with your twin, Grandma, it could be that he'd stowed away on an Atlantic steamer that stopped at Queenstown as you suggested, or maybe he was washed overboard at some point and was picked up by an Irish fishing boat.'

'Fascinating,' said the doctor. 'You have a good imagination Milly, but let's not get carried away. However, I suspect there is something in telepathy. It's beyond my understanding...' The doctor appeared to be mulling something over. 'It is possible, Mrs Martin, that your twin could have ended up in the ocean and received a few injuries but before he could drown, he was picked up by a boat. He could have ended up in Ireland on some lonely deserted farm. You never know, he could have met a girl and fallen in love. Or he could be living a new life in America. Sometimes the simplest explanations are the most likely.' He smiled wryly. 'All guesswork on my part,' he said. 'But now is the time for me to see some photographs of Joseph as a young man and compare him with your brother, Mrs Martin.' He opened the Bible once more and stared at the name on the flyleaf. 'I see your maiden name was Milburn. There is a hamlet named Milburn in the border country of England and Scotland.'

'Indeed so, I was told that by my brother. He was quite excited when he discovered the Milburns were border reivers way back in olden times.'

Feeling in a daze, Milly left the room again and went into the lounge where there was another album on a bookshelf. She returned to the morning room and placed it on the table in front of Doctor Fraser and looked over his shoulder. As he turned the pages, it struck her afresh just how alike her great-uncle was to her father in their younger days. Could it be that her grandmother had 'the sight' as the Celts called it and due to that link with her twin, she had seen him and not her father in her vision and was confusing the two? It was all so puzzling.

She said as much to the doctor and her grandmother.

'The human mind is hard to understand, but the links between twins are only just starting to be studied. As a man of science, I find all this incredible.'

'But aren't you also a man of faith?' asked Milly. 'If you prescribe a certain treatment for a sickness or disease, you have faith it'll work even if you don't always understand exactly how it works?'

He agreed. 'We've still some way to go before we have all the answers.' He rose to his feet and bowed slightly in Adelaide's direction. 'It's been a pleasure meeting you, Mrs Martin, and I will do my best to help Milly to find your son.'

She held out a hand to him. 'I believe you. You are a good listener, Doctor.'

He kissed the back of her hand lightly. 'Grief is a strange emotion, Mrs Martin. It can play all manner of tricks with us. It is a powerful thing but cannot always be trusted to lead us to the truth. Till we meet again, dear lady.'

Her cheeks pinked. 'I will pray for your success.'

Milly kissed her grandmother's cheek and followed the doctor to the door.

'Thank you so much, Doctor, your visit has given my grandma a lift.'

'It's all very perplexing, Milly. Your grandmother is very far from being a dotty old woman. There is much that science can't explain.'

If only it could, Milly thought, then Doctor Fraser bid her goodbye.

'It's high time I paid a visit to that granddaughter of mine,' he said.

She closed the door after him. Milly was still pondering over the day's events as she returned to her grandmother who was now drifting off to sleep in her armchair in the parlour.

Chapter Fourteen

In Liverpool the flu epidemic was starting to abate, and Milly thought it was high time that she paid Jimmy a visit to let him know that she was back.

The following Saturday, which was Susan's morning off, she had settled her grandmother in for her breakfast and then afterwards cleared away the crockery. Her grandmother was now reading the Saturday papers and Milly was getting ready upstairs because when Susan came back, she was going to take the tram to Liverpool.

Unexpectedly, Milly heard the jangle of the back door opening and closing so she darted down the stairs, hoping that it might be the postman with a letter, either from Andrew, or possibly from Jimmy, or it could be one of the delivery boys dropping in some groceries, she thought. She hoped it was a note from Jimmy, he wouldn't find it hard to work out where she lived through the Anderson family.

However, when she walked through the kitchen, she was surprised to see Violet Rogers there, who seem equally surprised to see Milly there too. 'Violet! What are you doing here? I've been meaning to call around to let you know that I'm back and can start my lessons again, but I don't have time today—'

However, Violet stopped her in her tracks when she said, a bit sheepishly, thought Milly, that it was Adelaide she had come to see. For the first time, Milly noticed that Violet had her twin boys in tow. They were around eight years of age, and both had equally snotty noses which they both wiped with their dirty cuffs.

'Mrs Martin is very keen on the boys, she likes twins and we've been popping in now and again.' Violet paused and looked more defiant now, jutting out her chin. 'She says they cheer her up.'

'Why didn't you come in through the front door? They don't have the flu, do they?' Milly asked.

'Of course not! I wouldn't drag them out if they were ill. We've been coming when Susan is off, there's nothing wrong with that. It keeps Mrs Martin company and she isn't left alone.'

Milly wasn't sure why Violet wouldn't come when Susan was there. Unless she didn't want Susan to know she was coming. She frowned, but didn't know what to say to that and stood back to let Violet and her sons through. However, Violet seemed to know exactly where she was going and headed straight for the morning room, without being invited to do so.

'Mrs Martin is expecting us.' Violet undid her coat and that of the boys and hung them quickly on the coat stand. Milly heard her grandmother exclaim in pleasure at their arrival before Violet gently pushed the door of the room shut behind her. Milly vowed to have a word with Susan about it the next time she had a chance.

At least she could get going a bit earlier, she thought, and headed out to get the tram.

–

A little while later, she arrived at Jane's house off West Derby Road and was delighted that not only were Kyle,

Jane and Siobhan there, but also, and a sight for sore eyes, was Jimmy.

'I met Jimmy on the tram yesterday and told him you were coming over today.' Jane smiled at Milly who suddenly felt a bit shy.

What's wrong with me, she thought, he's just a boy!

'My boss is down with the influenza,' he told her. 'There's no proper work until he's fit to come back, so I've been helping out a bit at the docks, though there's no work there today. Too many fellows already queuing up down there this morning.'

Milly felt secretly pleased that was the case, otherwise she might not have seen him at all.

Conversation turned to Siobhan and it seemed that Jane and Kyle were doing their best, along with May, to help Siobhan in her search for her father Mick O'Connor. While Jane and Siobhan had haunted the stage doors of Liverpool's theatres, Kyle had visited the pubs close by, hoping to hear a snatch of conversation that could prove useful in tracing Mick. They also read the local newspapers and *The Stage* theatrical paper, but so far, they had not struck lucky.

However, this morning Kyle had some news for them. 'May was looking through the *Liverpool Echo* and recognised a name in a piece about the Floral Pavilion in New Brighton which was a popular venue for revues and the like since before the war.'

'Didn't it used to be called the Victoria Pavilion then – an open-air theatre and gardens?' asked Jane.

'That's right. The theatre was closed during the Great War, opening afterwards to great acclaim and in 1925 a roof was constructed of iron and glass.'

'So, what has this to do with my daddy?' Siobhan said.

'Well, May recognised the name of the choreographer who had been the mutual friend of your dad, Mick O'Connor, and herself.'

'Then we must go and speak to him,' Jane said forcefully.

–

Jane wasted no time galvanising them all and they headed out that afternoon for a performance in the hope that this choreographer would have some news of Micky's present whereabouts. The five of them decided to take the ferry across the Mersey as it was a sunny, if cold, day as they set out for New Brighton. They could not have enjoyed the day out more.

Milly and Jimmy sat next to each other in the theatre as they watched Murray Ashford's review show, which included comedians, dancers and a sing-a-long which Milly loved, especially 'Oh Oh Antonio' and 'Ta-Ra-Ra Boom-De-Ay'. In the interval, Jimmy bought her an ice-cream while Kyle bought one each for Jane and Siobhan. Milly felt awful for thinking it but felt almost grateful for the flu as it meant she and Jimmy had got to spend the day together.

After the show, Kyle made discreet enquiries at the box office and told them that May had sent them. Her name seemed to open doors as the gentleman she had told them about came out to meet them and was able to explain that he had heard on the grapevine that Micky was performing at the Llandudno Palladium Theatre in the Welsh seaside town, during the next fortnight.

'So, he has been in Wales all this time?' Siobhan said.

'That may not be so, stage performers are always on the road,' the man told her. 'It may be that he went away and has gone back there again.'

On the way back home, the five of them talked about how Siobhan could be reunited with her father.

'It's not safe to go on your own,' said Kyle. 'I'd go with you but I've work.'

'I'm not allowed to have any time off from the hat shop, yet,' Jane said. 'I've not been there long enough.'

'That settles it,' said Milly. 'I'll come with you.'

'Not a chance,' said Kyle. 'I'm not letting two young girls go off on their own, it's not safe.'

'I could go with them,' offered Jimmy. 'My boss won't be well enough to come back to work for ages yet.'

Milly's eyes were shining at this news. 'That's all agreed, then,' she said, before Kyle could disagree. 'What will your mother say, though Jimmy?'

'What can she say? I'm a man now, and she can't stop me.'

Milly thought that wouldn't stop her trying.

–

A few days later, Milly and Siobhan were waiting for Jimmy at the station, but he was late.

'Where has he got to?' Milly said. 'We'll miss our train if he doesn't make it soon.'

At that moment, she caught sight of him striding across the ticket hall, accompanied by his mother, who was fussing around him as she tried to keep up with his brisk pace.

'Now, Jimmy, I'm not happy about you going off galli-vanting for no good reason. When will you be back?' Her lips were puckered in a pout, but Milly could see that in her eyes the woman looked quite afraid.

'We're only going to be there for one night. We just hope to be able to see Siobhan's father and come straight back in the morning.' Milly tried to reassure her.

'And where will you stay? You could end up on the streets!' Cathy looked like she was about to burst into tears. 'If something happens to you, I'll be all on my own.' Her voice was almost a wail.

Jimmy patted his mother's arm. 'Don't over-dramatise the situation, Mother, we're going to Llandudno, not Timbuctoo!'

After much more fussing, with Milly and Siobhan encouraging Jimmy along the concourse towards their platform, they were soon waving from the train to a tearful Cathy who waved her handkerchief at them forlornly.

'Why is your mother so fretful?' asked Siobhan as they removed their coats and hats and settled into the seats of their carriage. They were in their own little part of the carriage and Milly looked out of the window excitedly as the smoke from the train's coal-driven engines drifted past their window.

'She's never got over me dad's death. She sees disaster around every corner,' he told them both.

'Poor woman,' said Siobhan kindly. Milly thought how annoying it would be to have a person like that in one's life, never letting you get on with things.

'I've never been to the seaside proper before,' she told them both.

'You're in for a treat,' Jimmy said. 'Even in winter there'll be amusements and candy floss and the like.'

The journey passed quickly as they chatted about the difference between Ireland and England and Milly and

Siobhan mused over what their fathers had been up to if they might still be alive. It wasn't long before the northern Welsh coastline appeared to their right out of the window. It was a clear and bright day, cold but beautiful and Milly felt a sense of anticipation as they got off the train at Llandudno Junction to make the final stage to the town itself.

When they arrived, the town was much bigger than Milly had anticipated, and the sea spread out before them in a horseshoe shape with many grand houses and hotels lining the bay. Milly thought it was a wonderful place and was sorry she wasn't there in summer to make the most of it.

That afternoon they walked along the pier; many of the amusements were shut over the winter but they managed to find an arcade that was open and wasted a few farthings and halfpennies there along with the penny falls. Jimmy took his chances on the rifle range and Milly was thrilled when he shot down three tin cans in a row and won her a toffee apple, which she shared with Siobhan; both managing to get thoroughly sticky.

That evening they were virtually first in the seats in the back of the stalls at the Llandudno Palladium Theatre. There was more than one theatre in the town, but the one on the pier only did musical concerts and the Palladium was the one which seemed to specialise in the type of variety that Mick O'Connor was known for.

Siobhan had been beside herself with excitement when they had queued up at the ticket office and seen the poster with her father's name on it. 'I just hope he wants to see me.' She fretted.

'Of course he will,' reassured Milly.

The first few turns Milly gave perfunctory attention to and she began to get impatient, thinking they should have bought a programme, so they would have known when Mick O'Connor would take to the stage.

As it was it was not until after the interval and well into the second half that Mick O'Connor, Ireland's finest baritone, was announced. Milly sat up straight as a cheer went up; she did not want to miss a second of Siobhan's father's performance. She stared at the sprightly upright figure wearing evening dress, his salt and pepper-coloured hair slicked back, shiny with hair oil, his toothbrush moustache neatly trimmed. She clapped and spared a glance to where Jimmy and Siobhan were sitting along the row and smiled, guessing the girl would be as proud as Punch. Then, from the stage, Mick lifted a hand for silence.

The first song he sang was 'If I were a Blackbird' to which Milly knew the words because it was a very popular song. Then he sang 'Béal na Bláth' an Irish lament, and lastly he gave voice to the ever popular 'Danny Boy'. An encore was called for as he made to leave the stage and he allowed himself to be persuaded and sang 'The Black Velvet Band' before he left the stage.

'Let's get outside and wait for your father by the stage door,' said Jimmy to Siobhan.

'The show hasn't finished,' Siobhan said. 'Maybe you two should stay and meet me outside?'

A woman behind them hissed at them to be quiet and Milly noticed that there was a man was on stage whose sallies were being greeted by laughter. She guessed he must be a singing comedian and she heard Jimmy whisper, 'Let's all leave together, it's safer for Siobhan in case something goes wrong with her father.'

Shortly after the three of them rose and made their way to the exit and headed outside to the stage door at the rear of the theatre where admirers of the various acts had gathered in anticipation at getting their programmes signed by their idols. In response to Jimmy's questioning, with a tip and a written note given to him, the man on guard agreed to send the message to Mick O'Connor asking if his daughter and two friends could see him. He sent a young lad with the message who returned a short while later, saying he was to take them to Mr O'Connor's dressing room.

Milly almost danced along the passage leading to the dressing rooms, and as soon as her father caught sight of Siobhan as she entered his dressing room, he raced to her and scooped her up in his arms.

'Me poor darlin' girl,' he said, with tears in his eyes. 'I have heard all about your mammy in this letter that I received only yesterday.' He showed them the letter, which was from Jane, who had indeed written to him to tell him of his daughter's predicament. 'I only spoke to the theatre manager this morning and he was going to give me leave to come and get you, though I can see that won't be necessary.'

He and Siobhan embraced, and he told his daughter what had happened between himself and her mother. 'We didn't get on, as you know and were always quarrelling, especially about the O'Donnells who were an interfering and untrustworthy lot. In the end, when she wanted to live with them, I'd had enough.'

'Mammy came looking for you, Daddy. I think she was sorry and wanted to make up,' Siobhan said sadly.

'And now there's no chance of that as the flu has taken her. At least we have each other.' Mick held his daughter close to him.

Siobhan introduced Milly and Jimmy and explained Milly's connection to the O'Donnells.

'So, what is it that makes you believe Joseph could be alive?' asked Mick after being told about the search for Joseph. 'My wife wrote to me at the time that they were letting folk know that he was missing, he was believed slain in an ambush during the Irish Civil War.'

'That's what we were led to believe,' Milly said. 'But my grandmother doesn't believe it. She had a vision in which he was alive.'

Mick said, 'I'd say that's a mother's wishful thinking if I didn't know better. What if we get out of here and go and have a drink and a bit of supper. I know a place that'll fix us up.'

—

Within half an hour they were seated at a table in the public house next door to the theatre. Mick had a pint of Guinness and Jimmy a small Guinness shandy, while the girls were happy with lemonade as they were served bowls of the stew that was left over from earlier in the day, served with buttered crusty bread.

It was not until halfway through the meal that Micky laid down his spoon, had another mouthful of Guinness, and said, 'I drew close to your father, Joseph, when I was staying at the old O'Donnell's farm just before the fighting broke out in the summer of 1922. Joseph had just sent Bridget and Milly to his mother's in Liverpool and I told him he was a fool to stay behind and be dragged into the fighting. It was then he told me that he didn't intend doing much fighting but using the opportunity to try and discover what had happened to his mother's twin brother, Barnaby.'

'Presumably he told you about the special bond between them and how Barnaby had been in touch with his mother telepathically,' said Milly.

Micky shook his head. 'No, although in Ireland we don't mock the mystical as the English do. I offered my help, saying I could keep me ears and eyes open as I travelled around Ireland performing. He told me his uncle's name was Barnaby Milburn and apparently, this uncle did a bit of acting and impersonating and had wanted to go on the stage, but his own father forbade it.'

'But it was years before that Barnaby went to Ireland and nothing was heard from him afterwards. He seemed to have vanished into thin air,' said Milly.

'Well, would you believe I ran into him? Literally! It was in a boarding house in the north, Barnaby was coming down the stairs and I was going up. Later we had a drink and a crack, he told me his name, Bob Milburn, and that he had married an Irish girl from the north, but that he was originally from Lancashire, as if I couldn't have guessed from his broad accent. He was a good impersonator though and as Englishmen weren't so welcome at that time, he often used to pass himself off as an Irishman. It wasn't until he mentioned having a twin sister that I worked out that Bob Milburn was just his stage name and he admitted his real name was Barnaby. He told me he never travelled with his wife.'

'It must be the same person,' said Milly, unable to keep still with excitement.

'So, it was likely he was your father's uncle, he was sprightly for his age, but he must have retired now,' said Micky. 'The travelling company he was with moved on and although I'd see posters advertising the company he was part of, I never met him again.'

'So, Dad was searching for him with just the information you'd given him to go on,' said Milly. 'But Barnaby could be dead by now.'

'He could still be alive as well. He was a healthy, strong fella for his age,' said Micky

Milly nibbled her lower lip and her face screwed up in thought. 'But why couldn't Dad tell Mammy what he was up to?'

'He didn't trust the O'Donnells as there was money involved.'

'Not even Mammy?'

Micky nodded.

Milly remembered the tough days in Liverpool and what a difference some money would have made, but then she recalled that there would have been no cause for them to go short if they had continued living with her grandmother Martin.

'So, what do we do next?' she asked.

'We sleep on it and discuss it in the morning,' said Jimmy.

Chapter Fifteen

Siobhan stayed with her father in his lodgings and room was also found for Milly and Jimmy in the same boarding house. It was one of those places where the residents were turfed out at nine o'clock in the morning after a meagre breakfast of toast and margarine. It was bitterly cold and the pavements were slippery after a hail storm overnight, but by ten o'clock that morning the sky was blue and the sun shone brilliantly, so plans were discussed and telephone calls made from the foyer of the Grand Hotel where they all met for coffee. Milly was keen to let Andrew know she had found Mick O'Connor and he wouldn't need to make any enquiries on their behalf now, but she shrieked in excitement over the telephone when he told her that he was a father of a lovely girl and that mother and daughter were doing well, but the baby had come a little early. Andrew and Anne had decided on the name Christina Sarah for their daughter. Sarah having been his mother's name and Christina because the baby had been born so close to Christmas.

When she came off the telephone it was decided that she and Jimmy would return to Merseyside while Siobhan stayed with her father who would eventually return to Ireland.

Milly thought of her mother and asked Siobhan to give her love to Bridget, but not to mention to the O'Donnells that she had been searching for Joseph, a quest that would continue in the new year.

At the station they were bid a fond farewell from Siobhan and Mick. Milly and Jimmy spent the first part of the journey admiring the view from the window again, the sea was calm and the sun's rays sparkled on the surface.

–

When they arrived back in Liverpool, it was getting late so Jimmy suggested that they pop in and see Jane to tell her what they had learnt.

Milly rubbed her arms to warm them up as they slowly thawed out in Jane's kitchen off West Derby Road. Kyle was also there, and Milly noted that he had become a feature in Jane's house these days. She was happy that they were hitting it off. Milly told them both what they knew about Joseph's intention to find his Uncle Barnaby and about Mick O'Connor meeting Barnaby at a lodging house some years before.

Kyle looked flabbergasted, but then said, 'I bet Mick O'Connor didn't tell you that the aim in finding Barnaby is because half the money his mother has would have gone to him if he was found. Adelaide's probably worried that he might have a family somewhere and they're hard up. She wouldn't want to see them go without.'

Jimmy gave a low whistle. 'What a family – to go missing when there's a fortune waiting for you.'

'Wait a minute,' said Milly. 'Barnaby might not have been expecting anything. He fell out with his father and he wouldn't know of his mother's death.'

'He must surely know that his mother is dead after all these years. It could just be that your grandmother feels duty bound that they should have a fair share if he did have a family.'

Milly agreed, 'She'd rather they have it as she didn't want my mam or the rest of the O'Donnells to get their hands on it, even by accident. They're trying to persuade the courts to legally declare Daddy dead after all this time. If Grandma hadn't changed her will, my mammy might inherit it as one of Joseph's beneficiaries.'

'Perhaps you could put an advert in the Irish newspapers asking for news of Barnaby and any of his family,' suggested Jane.

'Do we know his surname?' asked Kyle.

'Yes, Milburn,' Milly said. 'He uses it on the stage.'

'Who's to say he mightn't be back over here?' said Jane.

'Surely he would try and see his sister if he was?' Jimmy suggested.

'But when he ran away, they were living up Lancashire,' Milly said. 'He wouldn't know where to find her. Besides, he could be dead despite what Mick said about him being fit and strong,' she added sadly.

'Let's not think the worst,' said Jane. 'Besides, we've yet to find either your father or your great-uncle Barnaby. You still have a big task before you.'

'And we still have Christmas to organise and celebrate.' said Jane. 'Milly, how about you spend it here with me, Kyle and May?'

'I'd like that,' said Milly. 'I'd like to see Jimmy too...' she smiled at him shyly, '...but I think I should spend Christmas with Grandma in Waterloo.'

'Of course,' Jane said. 'I wasn't thinking. It's getting late so both of you must stay for dinner and Milly you can go home tomorrow.'

Milly was grateful for the offer as she was dog-tired after the back and forth over the past few days. After a meal of cod in parsley sauce with potatoes and carrots, Jimmy headed for the door.

'Your mam will be having kittens and probably thinks you've been murdered in Wales,' she teased.

'Be nice,' he said. 'She can't help worrying, it's in her nature.'

'I know that, I'm starting to understand that a bit more,' she said apologetically. 'Thanks for coming with me.'

'I enjoyed it,' he said. 'Who doesn't like a mystery and besides, I like spending time with you.'

'So do I with you.' She smiled warmly.

'My mam and I are going to Southend for Christmas to see Aunt Sal, no doubt we'll see Andrew and Anne too.'

'I'm a bit jealous, I won't see you for ages, either.'

'Nonsense,' he said, 'I'll be back before you know it.' And Milly let him kiss her on the cheek before they said goodnight.

—

The next day, Milly walked up the front path through the gates to her grandmother's house, still thinking of Jimmy. She had given Jane a Christmas card to hand to him, wishing him and his mother a Happy Christmas in it.

It would be Christmas Day on Sunday and her grand-mother had no idea that she would be home in time for Christmas or that they would have the whole festive season together.

She had managed to pick up some Christmas presents that morning before travelling to Waterloo and juggled her shopping bags in her hands before banging the knocker. A few minutes later she heard hurrying footsteps advancing to the front door. A moment passed and the door was flung open to reveal a flustered Susan with a length of tinsel around her neck. She peered out and started. 'Is that you, Miss Milly?'

'It certainly is, Susan.'

'Thank God!' exclaimed the maid fervently.

'How is Grandma?' Milly did not wait for an answer but stepped around the housekeeper with her rucksack and Gladstone bag.

'The mistress is a bit low, not having heard from you and not really wanting me to go home to Mother and the family for Christmas. Although, that Violet Rogers would be glad to be rid of me.'

'What do you mean, Susan?' Milly asked, taken aback by the mention of her typing teacher's name and remembering Violet's previous unannounced visit.

'She's no shy Violet but a snake – worming her way into the mistress's good graces, going on about this house needing the sound of children's voices at Christmastime and offering to spend the festive season here with her husband and children to keep her company – going on about you and your father not caring about her because we've heard nothing from you.'

Milly said that she could scarcely believe it.

'Are you calling me a liar, Miss Milly?' said Susan, wrapping her hands in her apron and wringing it.

'Of course, not,' Milly hastened to reassure her. 'I can't understand it. I sent a postcard just to keep in touch, but we didn't have much to tell her until recently but now I have plenty.' She paused. 'Now help me in with my shopping and then let's make a pot of tea, as I'm parched, then we can talk to Grandma.' Milly paused to ask whether Violet was in the house now.

Susan shook her head. 'She persuaded your grandmother to hand over some money to buy some treats in for Christmas. I've been at my wits end, wondering what to do as the mistress won't listen to a word against her. I'd heard them talking and there was mention of something called Power of Attorney and that was something that had to be done in case you went missing, too, Miss Milly, with not having heard from you.'

Milly took a deep breath, having heard of Power of Attorney, and wondered what had happened to the postcard she had sent, but decided she had to set her concern about them aside for now and get to the bottom of this business with Violet. Was she really planning to usurp her place in her grandmother's affections? A couple of thoughts occurred to her.

'Susan, is it possible for your mother to come here for Christmas? I'm sure they would enjoy talking of the old days and she could help you to make some special Lancashire treats. I'll see she won't lose by it.'

Susan's eyes lit up. 'That would put Violet's nose out of joint. I'll telephone the post office and ask for a message to be sent to Mam.'

'Good! Meanwhile I'll get in touch with the orphanage and ask can they get a message to Kyle – he knows Violet's husband and hopefully will help us to sort this whole matter out.' She took a deep breath. 'Now I need to see Grandma.'

Susan took her to the morning room and left the two to talk while she brewed a pot of tea before phoning the village post office.

Milly sat at the breakfast table and gazed across at her grandmother. She was surprised to see she looked much better than she had done when she had left her.

'Hello, Grandma, how are you? I'm sorry to hear that you didn't receive the postcard I sent you, but I'm here now and have news for you.'

'What news?' Adelaide asked, while dabbing crumbs and marmalade from the corners of her mouth with a napkin.

'It's about your brother, Barnaby,' replied Milly.

'Barnaby! What about Joseph?' Adelaide leaned forward in her chair.

'We're still searching for him.' Milly sighed. 'It isn't easy. In fact, it's extremely difficult, but we struck lucky when we discovered that the father of a distant cousin of mine, whose name is Mick O'Connor, had met your brother years back when Barnaby was doing an impressionist act.'

'So, he had his own way eventually,' said Adelaide, smiling and leaning back. 'But why didn't he let me and Mother know?'

'We believe he married an Irish girl,' Milly told her.

'Does he have a family?' Adelaide's expression was happily excited.

'I don't know. What he told Mr O'Connor is that his wife is from the north and didn't travel with him, so maybe they did have children and she was at home with them, they'd all be much older now of course,' said Milly.

'You're going to have your work cut out finding them and Joseph,' Adelaide said.

'I know,' said her granddaughter. 'I'll go to Ireland in the spring if I have to, although Andrew's grandfather will be returning to his practice in Belfast sooner than that.

You might remember, Grandma, he's the Irish doctor who came to see you.'

'Why can't you go sooner?' asked her grandmother.

'Winter storms,' said Milly, trying to conceal her irritation at the idea her grandmother was expecting her to set off again with barely her feet having touched the ground. 'Besides which I thought it would be lovely to spend Christmas with you, Grandma.'

'You don't have to worry about me. That woman with the typewriter is coming here with her twins and her husband. It'll be nice to have a man about the place and hear the laughter of children. Perhaps you should stay with that friend of yours, Jane?'

Milly's heart sank. 'I wouldn't deny that children are wonderful, Grandma, but blood is thicker than water and Violet isn't family, is she?' she said coaxingly. 'Until Joseph and Barnaby and his family are found, I have no family but you.' She covered her grandmother's wrinkled, liver-spotted hand with her smooth, soft hand.

Indecision crossed the old woman's face as she gripped her granddaughter's hand. 'What if Barnaby were to die before you found him due to the delay?'

'You mustn't think like that,' Milly said, marvelling that her grandmother could think straight about the matter. 'We need to continue to pray and have faith.'

'You sound like your great-grandmother.' Adelaide sighed. 'So be it. I'm tired now. Accompany me to the drawing room and sit me by the fire. My magazines are on the occasional table. Violet brought me the Christmas editions.'

Milly settled her grandmother in an armchair beside the fire and brought her *The Lady's Companion*, *Nash's*

Pall Mall Magazine and the *Woman's Weekly*, thinking she would enjoy looking through them, herself.

As it was, her grandmother asked her to read a short story out of the *Woman's Weekly* to her. Milly knew she was not the greatest of readers due to the schooling she had missed but decided to have a go. She need not have worried as she had only been reading for ten minutes when her grandmother dozed off. A few minutes later she heard the door knocker sound and then Susan's hurrying footsteps, raised female voices and then more footfalls before Violet with her baby in her arms, entered the drawing room.

Milly lifted her gaze from the magazine and stared at Violet. They both started to speak at once. Then they stopped. Milly suggested they step outside and led her away from the drawing-room door and jumped in first with the words, 'I hear you've been keeping my grand-mother company again while I've been away. Do I thank you for doing so and accept you were doing your good deed for unselfish reasons – or am I right in thinking that there is something more going on?'

'Mrs Martin is a lonely old woman.'

'She has Susan.'

'A servant.'

'A caring housekeeper who has known Grandma all her life. You have no cause to look down on her.'

'She can't be a proper companion to your grandmother who is an educated woman, as am I,' said Violet.

'My grandmother was only educated as far as her middle-class father thought fit because she was a girl. She was expected to marry, run the household, bear children and most of all support her husband.' Milly sat down and indicated that Violet do the same. 'Why don't you tell me about your past before you came to Liverpool, Violet? Am I to take it that you've come down quite a way in the world since leaving Coventry?'

'My parents owned a silk ribbon factory that my grandfather on my mother's side founded. As she was an only child, she inherited it when he died and my father married her. My brother would have inherited if it had not been for cheap French imports which ruined our business. I kept the books as I inherited my grandfather's gift for figures.'

'I suppose your aim is to climb up in the world again?'

'Do you blame me, child, for wanting to do so?' Violet could not disguise the anger in her voice.

'Not at all,' said Milly mildly. 'But I am no child, what you are doing is wrong if it's at the expense of my father, uncle, cousins if I have any, not to mention Susan and myself.' She pushed herself up from the chair. 'I went to you for help, trusting Kyle's recommendation. I had every sympathy for you in your situation because I know what it is to be hard up and I wanted to help you in return.'

Violet released a pent-up breath. 'It's not my intention to push anybody out. But my family need a champion and your grandmother has offered to be one.'

'Then firstly, you must stop attempting to put a wedge between me and my grandmother. Secondly, I will welcome you and your family to spend Christmas Day here as I believe Grandmother is looking forward to having children in the house but you must get any idea out of your head about moving your family in permanently or anything to do with Power of Attorney. I have also invited Susan's mother to stay as I think her talking over old times with Grandma will be good for her.' Milly held out a hand. 'Do we have a truce?'

Violet nodded. 'We do. I had no plan to move here permanently, that must have been an idea she got into her head.' She added, 'Do you still plan on continuing your typing lessons?'

'Oh yes, but when that is depends on the coming week and how it goes,' said Milly, knowing that with all the recent twists and turns in her life, who knew what was going to happen next.

Chapter Sixteen

Later that day Milly was discussing food and drink with her grandmother and Violet, while glancing through *The Lady's Companion* in the drawing room.

'We must make eggnog,' said Adelaide. 'We always had it on Christmas Eve and there's a recipe for it in that magazine.'

'And what about real brandy butter,' suggested Violet. 'I haven't tasted that since I left Coventry.'

Milly flashed her a look. 'We mustn't overload Susan and her mother in the kitchen.'

'I'll be happy to help,' said Violet.

'We'll all muck in as it's Christmas,' said Milly. 'I bet Susan's mother will know how to make plum duff and one of those Lancashire favourites, Eccles cakes.'

'We'll have a capon for the main course and a leg of pork,' murmured Adelaide, smacking her lips.

'Has an order been put in with the butcher?' asked Milly.

'Ask Susan,' Adelaide said.

Milly went to the door, opened it and called Susan who responded with, 'I won't be a mo', Miss Milly,' she replied. 'There's somebody at the front door.'

Milly moved into the hall and followed Susan, waiting to see who was there. She was delighted when Jane and

Kyle appeared singing, 'Here We Come A-wassailing,' as the door was flung open.

'How lovely to see you both,' she said. 'Come in out of the cold!'

They stepped over the threshold and both hugged her. 'So, how are things?' asked Jane.

'I'll tell you everything later,' said Milly. 'Right now, we're in the drawing room discussing food and drink for Christmas.' She led the way once they had handed over their outdoor clothes to Susan, who had stood aside waiting to take them.

Violet was standing up when they entered and appeared slightly nervous as they glanced her way. 'Now you're here, I'll have to be going.'

'You don't have to rush away on my account,' said Jane.

'It's not that,' Violet said. 'I'm a married woman and have duties to attend to.'

'Of course,' said Jane. 'You'll be back again, soon.'

Violet nodded. 'Oh yes, Mrs Martin has been so kind as to invite me and my family here on Christmas Day.'

'How lovely,' Jane said, darting a sideways glance at Milly. 'Don't you have any other family back in Coventry who'd like to see you and the children?'

She hesitated before saying, 'I have an uncle and a cousin, but we haven't kept in touch. They were against me and my brother coming to Liverpool.'

'Isn't Christmas a time to make up old quarrels?' asked Jane.

'You don't understand,' said Violet, 'it was best I left and besides we've made a life as best we could in Liverpool.'

Milly who had been listening keenly while watching her grandmother's expression, could not help wondering what she was thinking. As for herself she was thinking of her half-brother, Charlie, and their mother and what Jane was saying about Christmas being a time for mending old quarrels. On the spur of the moment she decided to buy a Christmas present for him tomorrow and take it the same day which meant going into town tomorrow, Christmas Eve.

Hearing Violet say goodnight to Adelaide roused Milly from her reverie and she accompanied her to the front door. 'I presume we won't see you tomorrow,' Milly said. 'You'll have a lot to do with it being Christmas Eve, so see you Christmas Day with your husband and the children.'

Violet said in a small voice, 'Hopefully. Goodnight.' She hurried away before Milly could ask what she meant by that 'hopefully'. Slowly she walked back into the drawing room where she found Kyle sitting beside her grandmother, his expression intent as he listened to her talking.

Shortly after Susan brought in a light supper, setting trays down on two occasional tables. Afterwards Adelaide announced she was tired and asked Milly would she help her to bed. Milly did so with alacrity, it being the first time since she had returned that Adelaide had made such a request. As Milly brushed her grandmother's hair in front of the dressing table mirror, she reminded her of the times Adelaide had brushed hers the same way when she and her mother had lived with her.

'How is your mother?' asked Adelaide, surprising her with the question.

'I haven't been in touch with her since I left her grandfather's farm in Ireland,' replied Milly. 'But I might possibly hear something of her around this time. I'll be visiting Chinatown tomorrow where she used to have a job in one of the laundries.' Milly didn't mention calling in to see Charlie with a Christmas present. She didn't know what her grandmother would make of Bridget having a son with another man while her father's fate was still unknown. She doubted Adelaide would take the news well, but it wasn't her secret to share. Milly paused a moment to give her arm a rest from the hair brushing. 'You have lovely hair still, Grandma,' she said. 'It still has a bounce in it and it's pure white. You could stand-in for Mother Christmas.'

'Thank you, dear.' Adelaide twisted her head and glanced up at Milly. 'I've always been slightly fascinated by the Chinese and the country of China. When I was a girl, I remember reading a book about Marco Polo and his adventures in the Orient. I would have liked to have travelled and would have loved to ride on the Orient Express all the way to Istanbul, but it's too late now. I'm much too old.'

'Nonsense, Grandma. Where there's a will, there's a way. Perhaps you could begin by leaving the house and travelling into town with me tomorrow and afterwards doing some shopping, we can visit Chinatown together.' Milly thought there was no need to go into any detail about things with her, she could just say Charlie was the son of an old friend.

Adelaide gasped. 'Did your mother work in a Chinese laundry, then?'

'Yes,' said Milly. 'You might not want to believe it, but Mam ironed beautifully. She told me once that she loved ironing and making shirts and sheets and the like look crisp and neat.'

'Susan hates ironing,' said Adelaide. 'It would be nice if her mother liked ironing instead. I would take her on to take care of my clothes.'

'She mightn't want to leave the village for good,' Milly said, putting the brush down. 'Anyway, are you coming to town with me tomorrow? It'll do you good to have an outing.'

'I'll sleep on it and let you know in the morning,' said Adelaide, standing up and going over to her bed.

'It'll be fun,' said Milly tucking in her grandmother and kissing her cheek. 'God bless, sleep tight.'

'God bless,' said her grandmother sleepily. 'It is a comfort having you here.'

Milly crept out of the bedroom, closing the door noiselessly behind her.

Downstairs, Jane and Kyle were snuggled up on the sofa when Milly entered the drawing room.

'Your grandmother seems to have all her marbles there,' said Kyle.

'Maybe that's because you're staying with her, Milly,' Jane said.

Milly said, 'Well, she has just told me that it's a comfort having me here, and she told me things that I never would have guessed at, like wanting to travel to China. She thinks she's too old now. I told her differently, which was what I thought she wanted me to say.'

'What brought this about China on?' asked Jane.

'My telling her I was going to visit Chinatown to take a Christmas present to Charlie. It ended in my suggesting that she come with me, but there is no reason to give her any more information.'

'Did she mention your mother?' asked Kyle; Milly nodded.

Jane rose from the sofa. 'We'd better be going. You'll need a good night's sleep to cope with tomorrow.'

'Susan's mother's coming tomorrow but not Violet,' said Milly.

'I was surprised by what Kyle told me about Violet. I wouldn't have believed it of her.'

'She feels that a house like this is where she belongs,' said Kyle. 'She is a bit of a snob. I'll make sure I have a word with her husband the next time I see him.'

'But she does love her children,' said Jane. 'And one can't blame her for wanting more for them.'

'Difficult, though, when the country is in the middle of a Depression,' said Kyle. 'And her husband is a warehouse labourer at such a time. She should be thankful he's still earning.'

Milly said, 'And what about you two? Is there any good news I should know about? Such as an engagement?'

The couple exchanged glances. 'We were waiting until Christmas Day to announce it,' said Kyle looking at Jane lovingly. 'So, don't go telling anyone. Especially Andrew and Anne if you should ring them.' Milly crossed her heart and congratulated them before seeing them out.

'Merry Christmas!' She waved to them before shutting the door and bolting it top and bottom, saying goodnight to Susan before going upstairs to bed.

–

The following morning, Christmas Eve, she was up early and went straight to her grandmother's bedroom. She was propped up with several pillows and drinking tea. Milly sat sideways on the bed and asked her whether she felt up to going into Liverpool to do a little shopping and then to visit Chinatown. For an instant, Adelaide looked puzzled and then she said slowly, 'Yes, I told you I was always interested in China. I feel a little stronger today so we shall go together.'

Milly beamed at her. 'It'll do you no end of good to get out.'

At that moment, there came a knock on the bedroom and a voice said, 'It's Susan. Are you wanting me to dress you, Madam?'

Milly went and opened the door and waved Susan inside. 'We're going to town, so if you could help get Grandma ready, that would be good. I'm going to dress myself now.'

Milly wasted no time washing, dressing and going downstairs for breakfast. She and her grandmother left the house within the hour and went and caught the train into Liverpool city centre. Her grandmother was a little slow, but Milly was surprised at her stamina. They went to Lewis's department store and ended up in the lift to the toy department where they wandered around for a while, despite there not being much on display what with the Depression. Eventually, Milly bought a Tri-ang toy truck with a winch, as well as one of the increasingly popular wooden jigsaws and a story book. 'I'm buying them for a little boy I know in Chinatown,' she told her grandmother. Once they were parcelled up, she led her grandmother out of the store and up Renshaw Street, turning into Berry Street, and eventually into Pitt Street.

They hadn't been walking for long when she spotted a boy who looked like Charlie kicking a ball about with some other boys. It was some years since she had seen her little half-brother, but with his half-Chinese and half-Irish features, he was easy to recognise, despite being much taller than she remembered him and was now around seven or eight years old. She called to him and almost immediately he saw her and came jogging over.

He looked confused for a moment, not recognising her, but Milly reached out to him and said, 'It's me Milly, don't you remember?'

Realisation dawned on the young boy's features, 'Milly, is it really you?' he said, stopping a few feet away.

'Of course, it's me,' she said huskily, tears blocking her throat as she held out her arms to him.

He threw himself into them. 'I told her I'd see you again one day.' His voice was muffled against her coat.

'You mean your grandmother?'

He shook his head. 'No, Mam! She's here in Liverpool staying at a bed and breakfast on Mount Pleasant.'

Milly was shocked, not knowing what to say, but Adelaide was straight at her shoulder. 'Mam? Is this Chinese boy some relation to you, Milly? Is that why we have come here today.'

Milly suddenly felt foolish, she should have known all along that it would be hard to keep Charlie's identity a secret. But before she could answer, Charlie piped up, 'Milly is me sister and we have the same Mammy, my daddy is Mr Chin.'

Milly registered the shock on her grandmother's face. 'Milly, why did you keep this a secret from me? Is this true?'

Milly nodded her head sadly, 'Don't think too badly of Mammy, she's headstrong and got caught up in opium. Mr Chin wasn't a bad man.'

Milly's heart began to beat heavily, and she thought she might faint as she drooped over Charlie. Adelaide who had not been able to take her eyes from Charlie, seized hold of her granddaughter's shoulder.

'I care nothing about this Mr Chin. I thought your mother was bad enough but now to discover that she had an illegitimate child with a man who runs a Chinese laundry. Milly I'm surprised at you for defending her.'

The words were enough for Milly to jerk herself upright. 'If Mam is in Liverpool, then I must go and see her.' She breathed out the words before clutching Charlie's coat tighter. 'Do you know the name of the bed and breakfast, Charlie?'

'I can take you there,' he said. 'I'll just tell me mates to let Granny know where I've gone.'

Milly watched him run to his friends and do as he said he would before he came running back to her. On the way to Mount Pleasant, Milly's grandmother walked in stony silence, though Milly noticed that she was not unkind to Charlie and asked after his schooling; Charlie told her that he had started school and liked it. They stopped at the foot of a flight of steps leading to the front door of a lodging house called the Arcadia.

'I insist on going in with you, Milly,' said Adelaide.

'Of course,' said Milly. 'I'd hardly expect for you to wait outside while I speak to Mam.'

'I intend to confront her,' Adelaide said, fiddling with one of her gloves.

'You could try turning the other cheek,' said Milly. 'Mam loves Charlie and whichever way you look at it, she was on her own in the world. She attracts trouble but I don't think she means to.'

Adelaide smiled grimly, 'You give your mother too much credit.' She pressed the doorbell.

A few minutes later it was opened by a youth who smiled and said, 'Can I help you?'

'We'd like to speak to Mrs Bridget Martin,' said Milly. 'I believe she is staying here. I'm her daughter Mildred.'

'Step inside,' he said. 'You can wait in the smoking room while I see where she is.' He led them to a room on the right and offered to bring them coffee.

Adelaide thanked him and sat down in an easy chair close to the electric fire he had switched on. Milly sat in the opposite chair and Charlie sat crossed-legged on the rug at her feet. They did not have to wait long before the coffee was brought, and it was Milly who noticed there were three cups and a glass of orange juice for Charlie. The youth told them that Mrs Martin would be with them shortly. He had no sooner left the room than there came the tap-tap-tap of heels on linoleum that paused outside the door, then it was pushed open and Bridget entered. A clear-eyed but anxious-looking Bridget stared at them.

'Hello, Mammy!' Milly stood up, delighted to see her mother despite all that had passed between them, while her grandmother proceeded to pour coffee into three cups.

'Milly, I'm so glad to see you safe and looking well,' said Bridget crossing the room quickly and holding her daughter in her arms.

'I've had a lot of practise in taking care of myself,' Milly responded. 'Charlie's looking well, too. It seems we did the right thing separating, so what are you doing over here, Mammy? I thought you were content living with your family in Ireland.'

'It has its drawbacks,' admitted Bridget. 'As for why I'm here, I came in the hope of seeing you and Charlie and wishing you a happy Christmas. I also need to let you know that I'm going to get married again.'

'Married!' exclaimed Adelaide. 'But you're married to my son!'

Bridget stared at her and said scornfully, 'Time you woke up to the truth, woman. Joe has been missing for a decade now and I'm going to see about him being declared dead officially.'

'But—!' started Adelaide, only to clamp her lips together at a look from Milly.

'So, who are you marrying Mam?' asked Milly in shock. 'Anyone I know?'

'I doubt it. His name is Sean and he lives in Dublin. I knew him years ago, long before I met your dad. He owns a large laundry and has the contracts for a lot of the big places in the city, such as hospitals, restaurants, hotels. The family are going mad about it, they thought I should persuade you to return to the farm, believing that one day either you or me could make them rich. I told Uncle Willie to grow up and help make the farm pay more by getting off his backside and do some work.'

Milly shuddered at the mention of her uncle. 'I bet there was a right barney,' she said.

'You can believe it,' Bridget said with a smirk. 'But I had Granddad behind me and for once he opened his mouth and let fly a few choice words at Willie. Whatever you might think of me, Adelaide Martin, I care nothing about your money. If I did, I could have put up with your high-and-mighty ways, just to line my pockets, but I didn't.'

There was little that Adelaide could say to this and she just pursed her lips in annoyance.

'I wish I'd been there to hear Granddaddy give him what for,' said Milly. 'When's the wedding?'

'Sean wanted it on Christmas Day, "better the day, better the deed", he said. But I persuaded him to change his mind, told him I wanted my daughter to be my bridesmaid.'

Milly's mouth fell open in disbelief. 'You are joking?'

Bridget shook her head. 'I love you, girl. I mightn't always have been a good mother to you and Charlie, but I really want you there to see me make good. There was a time when we were all the other had after your father disappeared.'

'Sorry to break up this lovely reunion, but Bridget, I'm still in shock to discover you're the mother of an illegitimate baby. Milly, you can't agree to be her bridesmaid,' interpolated Adelaide.

'I'd been on my own for years before Charlie was born, if your precious son is still alive, then he was a terrible husband leaving me and Milly to fend for ourselves. Perhaps if you'd been a more forgiving mother-in-law, we wouldn't have ended up on the streets.' Bridget said accusingly and Milly thought it hadn't taken them long to get back to their cat-fighting.

'How dare you blame me!' said Adelaide in outrage. 'You can't marry again anyway – you're still married to my son by law.'

'There's blame on both sides,' Bridget told Adelaide. 'I never cared about money, whatever you or the O'Donnells think. That's why I'm marrying Sean, he doesn't blame me for my past. Joseph will either be declared dead or I'll get a divorce on the grounds of abandonment.'

Adelaide seemed to go white at this news.

'My wedding will be on St Patrick's Day,' said Bridget. 'Milly, I hope you'll agree to be there as my maid of honour.'

Milly felt conflicted for a moment, she had come to be very fond of her grandmother, but she only had one mother no matter what had passed between them previously, and she made the decision there and then.

'I'll be there,' she said. 'Keep me informed about everything. Address letters to me at Jane Fraser's address.' She paused and wrote the address down in block letters and handed the paper to Bridget. 'Now let's drink our coffee and you can tell me all about this man.' The words were hardly out of her mouth when her grandmother let loose a volley of anger, called her granddaughter and her mother ungrateful and selfish, then she stormed out of the room shouting for someone to call her a taxi.

Milly said, 'I think there goes my Christmas dinner, bed and inheritance. Poor Grandmother, she'll be telling everyone I'm a terrible disappointment to her.'

'You could stay here at my expense,' said Bridget. 'I'll be leaving this afternoon to spend Christmas Day with Sean.'

Milly said, 'Give him my best wishes.' She took a mouthful of coffee before adding, 'I have friends and I'm sure Jane will take me in.'

'She's the one whose address you have given me.' Bridget tapped the folded sheet of paper with a fingernail.

Milly nodded, refilled their coffee cups and settled down with her mother for a good gab. They had both almost forgotten about Charlie and then he piped up and asked for a biscuit. Bridget pressed a bell on the wall by the mantelpiece and the youth appeared and shortly after he reappeared with a plate of homemade biscuits. Despite all the upset of the afternoon, Milly had missed her mother and the afternoon passed happily.

Chapter Seventeen

'So, is the search for your father going to be called off now?' Jane asked, handing Milly a cup of cocoa.

'I don't know what to do,' said Milly, warming her hands on the cocoa cup and settling comfortably on Jane's sofa. 'I'll see what Andrew has to say when I ring up on Boxing Day.'

'It sounds sensible to me,' said Jane. 'What are you going to do about your grandmother and Christmas Day tomorrow? Are you still going to stay there?'

'If you don't mind, I'll go to the Watchnight Service at Saint Faith's church where she might attend with Susan and her mother. I'll play it by ear, see how she reacts to my being there if they see me.' Milly took a large gulp of the early evening cocoa. 'She's unlikely to tear a strip off me in church.'

'Let's hope not,' Jane said. 'I do feel sorry for her.'

'So, do I. It's difficult knowing where my loyalties should lie.' She paused. 'I wish Daddy had thought of that when he chose to stay in Ireland, instead of coming to England with me and Mammy.'

'Perhaps he must have felt strongly about the political situation that was tearing Ireland apart. After all our government was divided too,' said Jane.

Milly remembered what Mick O'Connor had told her about Joseph attempting to find out what had happened to Barnaby. 'I'd just like to know if he's dead or alive. I wonder what would happen to Mam's new marriage if Daddy turned up alive afterwards?'

'If he'd been declared legally dead, then I should image your mother's second marriage would stand,' said Jane.

'What if Daddy still loves her?'

Jane pulled a face. 'Then why did he not come back? It's an awful lot of 'what ifs'. It's all surmising on our part. Whatever the truth, we can't change it,' said Jane, lifting a curtain to see what the weather was like. She gasped. 'I'd forget going anywhere if I were you, the fog's thickened. I hope it clears by tomorrow.'

'So much for Charlie and his mates praying for snow.' Milly sidled next to Jane and gazed out. 'At least I have a good excuse for not turning up at Grandma's. And I doubt if Violet and her husband would take their children in this.'

'I bet there'll be in increase in chest complaints because there's bound to be some people who risk making visits on foot in this weather,' said Jane.

'I think Kyle will still turn up here for Christmas lunch,' said Milly. 'He'll be wanting to be with you, and he might have spoken to Andrew on the telephone.'

'The telephone exchange will be over-worked,' said Jane gloomily. 'There could be queues outside telephone boxes. Let's put the radio on. There might be a play on or a festive show and no doubt there'll be a religious service on around eleven thirty.'

So, the radio was switched on to the *Light Programme* and they settled down in front of the fire and were soon laughing over the jokes of the comedian, Sandy Powell, whose catchphrase was 'Can you hear me, Mother?' Then there were Christmassy songs sung by Leslie Hutchinson and later there was music by Jack Hilton and his dance band.

They went up to bed after the Watchnight Service on the radio and Milly lay awake for a while, thinking of her family and of Jimmy, sending them wishes for a peaceful Christmas wherever they were at that moment. She woke to the sound of movement in the other bedroom and forced her eyes open to see that it was daylight. She wasted no time rolling out of bed and going over to the window where the curtains were not completely drawn and peered out. She let out a tiny cheer when she saw that she was able to see the backs of houses through a misty drizzle. She dressed and went downstairs and lit the fire.

After while she was having a wash-down at the back-kitchen sink, when Jane came downstairs. 'Merry Christmas! I see the fog has lifted somewhat,' she said. 'Have you made up your mind whether to go to your grandmother's or not?'

'Merry Christmas to you too, I was thinking whether to wait until after you've telephoned Andrew and see what he has to say.'

'You mean about whether to carry on the search for your father?'

'Yeah, and then I can speak to Grandma about it. Besides which I bought her a Christmas present and it's in my bedroom there. I should give it to her.'

'You'll have breakfast here before you go?' said Jane.

'If you don't mind.' Milly came through out of the back kitchen drying her face with a towel. 'I need to go to the house anyway, because yours and Kyle's presents are also there. I'll go as soon as I know what Andrew has to say.'

Decision made, Milly fried bacon and egg for their breakfast while Jane washed and donned the dress she had bought to wear on Christmas Day.

'The colour cerise suits you,' said Milly when Jane seated herself opposite her at the table.

'Have you bought anything new to wear for today?' asked Jane.

'Yeah, but it's at Grandma's, so I'll just have to wear my Sunday best to go there,' replied Milly.

As soon as she had finished her breakfast Milly went upstairs and dressed in the kilt and Fair Isle sweater she had bought out shopping when staying at Fiona's and Sandy's house in Edinburgh. As well as the tweed jacket, she had purchased and a woollen bobble hat that kept her head lovely and warm. Then she pocketed her purse and went downstairs and drank a milky coffee while she waited for Kyle to arrive.

He came half an hour later with presents, chocolates, a couple of bottles of beer and a bottle of sparkling wine. She had to wait another ten minutes while he and Jane wished each other a lovey-dovey happy Christmas. Only then did he tell them what Andrew and Anne had advised after congratulating him and Jane on their engagement.

'He thinks you should leave it to his grandfather to make enquires in Northern Ireland as he has a few ideas where to look and as for the Republic of Ireland forget searching there for now.'

Milly pulled a face and asked no more questions but wished Kyle a happy Christmas and said she'd see them later and left to catch a tram into town and then a train to Waterloo of which there was a reduced service.

She felt slightly on edge as she approached her grand-mother's house and after banging the knocker, she could not keep still but was hopping from one foot to the other. Then she heard the bolts being drawn back and the door opened to reveal Susan.

The housekeeper's face broke into a smile. 'You've come! The mistress wasn't sure you would after your falling out.'

'Is she still angry with me?' Milly stepped over the threshold.

'I'd say irritated more than angry. She can't make sense of yours or your mother's actions.'

'Will she want to see me?'

'Oh, I think so. It'll do her good to talk the situation over with you.'

'You do surprise me,' Milly said, removing her jacket. 'Have you heard anything from Violet? Is she here?'

Susan shook her head. 'She sent a telegram. Apparently, her cousin has been in touch with her. Their uncle passed away unexpectedly and he'd like her to go to the funeral.'

Milly was surprised. 'Doesn't he know it's Christmas and she has a husband and children?'

'Of course, he does. He's a widower, and he's no other relatives and he insisted that he needs a female relative to act as hostess and arrange the funeral meal.'

'He's got a nerve.'

'I agree, so does the mistress and my mam. Anyway, she's gone off to Coventry, leaving her kids and husband to fend for themselves. Although, the husband does have good neighbours. No doubt they'll help him with the children.'

'The selfish so-and-so. I bet there's money involved somewhere,' said Milly.

'You're right. The factory in Coventry was owned jointly by her father and this uncle. But the business went under, she's hoping her uncle will have done the decent thing and left her and her cousin what she reckons they're owed.'

Milly wondered if Violet's husband and her children would see any of the money. In the meantime, she needed to talk to her grandmother and try to smooth things out with her. She was in luck as her grandmother did not want to rake over what they had said to each other the day before.

'Your mother has always had the knack of riling me,' Adelaide said. 'I can't pretend it wasn't a shock to find out about your half-brother, and that she wants to remarry, but I've more important things on my mind. Here, take a look at this letter I received yesterday from my solicitor.'

Her grandmother handed her a letter which had the name of a firm of solicitors at the top. She read it quickly and then gasped. 'It says that they have had a correspondence from a gentleman in Ireland who claims to be your brother, Barnaby!'

'Yes,' said Adelaide. 'I called my solicitor yesterday, as soon as I received it. Some time ago he placed an advertisement in a few of the Irish newspapers, asking if anyone had any information about two missing persons, one Barnaby Milburn and the other a Joseph Martin. The news he had was to tell me that he'd had a letter from my brother explaining that he had stowed away on a ship when he was a young and made a life for himself out there. Now he is getting older, he wants to put the record straight and claim his inheritance.'

'Can he prove his identity?' Milly asked.

'That's what my solicitor is trying to find out. I've asked for a photograph. I'll be able to recognise him instantly as he'll look very like me.'

Milly bit her lip, this was an interesting development, but why had Barnaby chosen to come out of the blue now, just as they were looking for him? She handed the letter back to her grandmother. 'What happens now?'

'My solicitor will be in contact again when he has more evidence. My dear, this could put an end to my endless wondering about him and we'll finally know the truth.'

Milly nodded, that would indeed be a marvellous thing and it might even lead them a bit closer to finding out about her own father.

'Let's put all of that aside for now,' Adelaide said. Milly noticed that her grandmother was wearing a rather nice matching skirt and top in a purple- and green-flecked fabric that looked to be cashmere and she complimented her on her appearance.

Adelaide preened herself and said, 'Thank you, dear. How are your friends, Mr Anderson and Miss Fraser?'

'Full of the joys of the season. They've just announced their engagement, so Mr Anderson telephoned Miss Fraser's brother, Andrew and his wife, to tell them. Andrew told him that his grandfather whom you've met is going to make some more enquiries in the search for Daddy in Northern Ireland in the new year, so we'll just have to wait and see,' said Milly, and changed the subject. 'Can I just go upstairs and fetch your Christmas present, Grandma?'

'Of course. I have a present for you, too. I also bought presents for Violet and the twins. I thought they'd be here by now.'

'They won't be coming,' said Milly. 'Her uncle in Coventry has died and she's gone down there to the funeral.'

'What a shame! I was looking forward to seeing the children's faces when they opened their presents. I like children. Maybe she'll bring them to visit when she returns.'

Milly remained silent and left the room and went upstairs. She felt pulled two ways. She also would have enjoyed seeing the children's faces when they opened their presents. On the other hand, she felt concerned about her grandmother getting too fond of Violet's children as she could end up getting hurt. If only Joseph had not stayed in Ireland and instead come to Liverpool with her and her mother. They just might have provided her grandmother with more grandchildren and herself with brothers or sisters which would have made all the difference.

Milly was relieved that her grandmother was pleased with her Christmas gift, which was a wicker basket containing several items, all individually wrapped and tied up with different coloured ribbons. There were chocolate bon-bons, a pair of tan-coloured kid gloves, Coty's Lily of the Valley talcum powder, and a year's subscription to Boot's lending library, all bought with money her grandmother had given her. Milly knew she really had to start earning her own money, as soon as she could, but she did not kid herself that it would be easy. She'd talk to Violet about resuming her typing lessons when she returned, after all, she had a week's lesson in lieu she reminded herself.

–

That afternoon, over the preparation of the Christmas dinner in the kitchen, she mentioned the subject of getting a job, though could not think of anything that she was good for and said as much to Susan and her mother. Susan's mother was a small, tidy woman like her daughter with a kind twinkle in her eyes, and Milly could see it was a good idea to have asked her to come as she and her grandmother had spent much of the time reminiscing about their childhoods in Lancashire.

Susan's mother smiled. 'Why go looking for a job when you could have one here being a companion to your grandmother? She never went out to work but stayed at home, helping her mother. She only left home when she married your grandfather.'

'But times have changed,' Milly said.

'You can say that again,' said Susan. 'If I wasn't so fond of your grandmother, I'd have found myself a job in a factory where I could earn more money and have the company of other women.'

'You'd have difficulty doing so while there's a Depression,' said her mother. 'But it is time you found yourself a husband.'

'What man is going to want to take on a wife and start a family right now?' Susan said. 'Besides which there's more single women than men, so I'd either have to find myself one much younger or a lot older than myself. I'm going to end up an old maid.'

Milly thought of Jimmy and wondered if he had found himself another girl to keep him company while he was down south. She hoped not and left Susan and her mother in the kitchen and returned to the drawing room to her grandmother who was fiddling with the knobs of the radio.

'I'm trying to get the Light Programme,' said Adelaide.

'Shall I have a go?' asked Milly.

Her grandmother nodded. 'And if you could pour out a cream sherry for me?'

Milly poured out the sherry first and after handing it to Adelaide, set about finding the station. On recognising a well-known comedian's voice, she stopped twiddling the knob and listened.

'Isn't that George Formby?' she asked.

'It certainly sounds like him,' Adelaide said. 'But is it the father or the son? I've heard recordings of both.'

'If this is a live broadcast, it has to be George junior as his father died at the beginning of the 1920s. He's a Lancashire lad.'

'There's a lot of talent in Lancashire,' said Adelaide. 'I wish your great-grandfather had been behind Barnaby. It would be wonderful if your dad did come across him in Ireland.'

'Would they recognise each other, though?' Milly asked.

'Now there's a question,' said Adelaide, holding her feet out to the crackling fire.

Milly said, 'I sometimes wonder if I'd recognise Daddy. It's that long since I've seen him, and I was only little at the time.'

'We had some lovely Christmases when he was a little boy and your grandfather was still alive.'

'Grandma, I know you are cross with me about Mammy but I still want to live here with you. We could do more things together, such as visit Boot's lending library where you could choose books and I could read them out to you when the weather is bad, or if the weather is good, we could have days out to Southport or Liverpool or even Ormskirk or Burscough.' She paused. 'I did even wonder if you thought it would be a good idea if you bought an

206

automobile and I learnt to drive. We could even go further afield.'

Adelaide stared at her. 'Of course, you must continue to live here, and I like the idea of getting out and about. I enjoyed our trip into Liverpool yesterday despite everything and I'd like to get out more. I will enquire about a driver who can take us and I will seek a recommendation from a friend of mine whose husband has an automobile. I don't know why I never thought of it before.'

Milly said that she thought that was an excellent idea, especially as there were so many men out of work. Although, learning to drive herself would have been a feather in her cap, she had to accept that her grandmother was more of the old school who preferred a man being in charge when it came to motors.

–

It was to be several weeks before a shiny black Bentley made an appearance on the drive of the house, driven by a man called Leo who was fair-haired and blue-eyed with a fresh complexion and a sturdy-looking body. He had worked on one of the farms on the Duke of Westminster's estate in Cheshire for a number of years and had become adept at using farm machinery and acting mechanic and driver for the farmer's wife and children, though he'd recently been laid off as the farmer was struggling financially. He came highly recommended as being honest, respectful, dependable and intelligent. He was accepted as part of the household immediately and Adelaide was wont to say she never regretted purchasing the automobile for a moment and hiring Leo.

Despite Leo spending little time in the house during the cold short days of January, the atmosphere completely altered. His lodgings were in rooms that had been converted into a flat over the stables which was now used as a garage. His temperament was such that his presence lifted the gloom that had beset Adelaide over the years since losing sight of her twin, then her husband and then her son. Although she cared for her granddaughter, she was a woman who preferred the company of the opposite sex as she found them more interesting and challenging than her own.

So, it was that she had him take her for a drive most afternoons and on occasions Milly was invited along as well. She accepted without comment being ushered into the back while her grandmother sat in the front passenger seat. Milly listened to her grandmother chattering away to Leo, asking him questions about his childhood and why he had settled in the north west of England. Apparently, he was an orphan and had spent the early years of his life in an orphanage in Cumberland. After that he had worked as a farmhand on different parts of the Lakes and in Lancashire, gaining experience and meeting different people.

The weeks passed swiftly; Jimmy had returned from down south and with his boss now fully recovered from the flu, there were less opportunities for Milly and Jimmy to see each other though they had gone to the flickers a couple of times; once to see a Laurel and Hardy comedy and the other time to see Boris Karloff in *The Mummy* which frightened Milly a bit, and she had snuggled up to Jimmy in the seat.

Milly found herself thinking more and more about her mother's wedding. She visited Jane twice weekly and on a visit one evening at the beginning of March, Jane handed her an envelope. Milly recognised her mother's handwriting immediately and tore the envelope open and read the enclosed letter slowly.

She glanced across at Jane. 'It's from Mam. She wants me to meet her in Dublin the first Saturday in March to go shopping for my bridesmaid's dress and to meet her future husband.'

'You are going to go?' said Jane.

'Yeah, Mam and I went through a lot together after the news came about Daddy being missing and leaving his mother's house – and it's not as if I've had any good news about my father.'

'But you do know your great-uncle Barnaby could still be alive,' Jane said. 'Has there been any news from the solicitor?'

Milly shook her head. 'Not yet.'

'So, will you tell your grandmother you're going to Dublin?' asked Jane.

'I'll decide after I've spoken to the family solicitor, Mr Lancaster. He wrote to me asking me to call at his office in Castle Street this coming Thursday afternoon.' She paused. 'I wonder why he wants to see me.'

'I'll go with you as it's half-closing day, and you can come and have tea with Kyle, Aunty May and me afterwards,' said Jane, who was just as curious.

'I'd like that,' said Milly. 'I'll buy some cakes on the way.'

'No need, I'll bake,' said Jane. Milly did not argue but decided to buy Jane a bunch of flowers from one of the flower women in Clayton Square as way of thanks.

–

Milly was feeling extremely nervous as she and Jane entered the building in Castle Street and climbed the stairs to the third floor where the solicitor's office was situated. They were not kept waiting long before his secretary showed them into his office.

He shook them both by the hand and bid them be seated. 'No doubt you're very curious as to why I should want to see you,' he said, toying with the fountain pen on the blotter on his desk. 'But I've tried speaking to Mrs Martin and she just won't take what I say seriously.'

'What won't she take seriously?' asked Milly.

'The person that came forward as her brother, I do not believe to have a credible case. After receiving the initial letter from the supposed Barnaby Milburn, I made further enquiries and asked for a recent photograph at the address provided, this is what I received by return of post.'

Mr Lancaster took a photograph out of an envelope on his desk and handed it over to her. Milly felt her hand tremble as she took it; Jane leaned in to look as well. The photograph showed an elderly man, maybe in his sixties and though the photograph was in black and white, he clearly bore no resemblance to her grandmother, or indeed to how she remembered her father looking.

'But this can't be my great-uncle, he looks nothing like my grandmother, or any member of the family from old photographs,' she said, in puzzlement.

'This was my thought too, Miss Martin, however, they have sent a birth certificate which seems to be the correct one.' He handed that to them, too.

'The date looks about right, how could they have come by this?' Jane questioned.

'I intend to get the bottom of it, never you mind that, but when I voiced my concerns to your grandmother, she refused to accept that there could be a fraudster at work. I'm worried that she'll accept any Tom, Dick or Harry as her brother, just to ease her mind.'

'We met a man recently who said he had met Grandmother's twin brother some years ago. He was performing on the stage and was travelling from place to place, so he said. What do you want us to do?' Milly asked.

'Don't let her get carried away. I'll find proof that this is a hoax, but please help me persuade her that this is a red herring.'

Milly promised the solicitor that she would, but it seemed that he had something else to tell her.

'Are you aware that the courts have been considering declaring your father dead?' he asked her solemnly.

Milly felt her legs start to shake under the table, and she suddenly felt a great fear that he was going to tell her that the men in wigs at court had decided her daddy was dead, but instead the solicitor surprised her.

'The courts have decided that there is not enough evidence to declare him dead. However, they accept that your mother has been abandoned and have granted her a divorce, so she is free to marry.'

Milly blinked in surprise. So, they weren't sure her daddy was dead either? She felt hope flutter in her heart. It also meant that her mother would be free to marry again, though it would put to bed any talk of her inheriting the Milburn money.

Milly and Jane exchanged glances. 'Has my grandmother mentioned that my mother is remarrying?' asked Milly.

'She has indeed,' he replied, 'and that she does not want you to attend the wedding as your mother wishes. I feel it only fair to inform you that she has threatened to remove you as one of the benefactors from her will if you do attend your mother's wedding.'

Milly's fingers curled into the palms of her hands where they rested in her lap. 'She and my mother never could bear one another, I often felt like a piggy in the middle after Daddy sent us to live with her.'

'What is your decision, if you don't mind my asking?' he asked.

'I have every intention of attending my mother's wedding. She deserves some happiness. Only this morning I received a letter from her asking me to meet her in Dublin to shop for my bridesmaid dress. The wedding is on St Patrick's Day, the seventeenth of March. Most likely I'll stay with Mammy during the ten days in the run-up to the wedding.'

'So, you'll travel to Dublin on the third of March?' he said.

Milly nodded. 'I confess to looking forward to doing so, but not having a confrontation with Grandma about it.' She glanced at Jane. 'That's why I was going to ask can I stay with you for a few days before I take the ferry.'

'Of course, you can but you must write a note for your grandmother to read after you've left and thank her for all her generosity to you.'

The solicitor regarded her. 'How is the search for Master Joseph progressing?'

Milly said, 'We have no news about my father but Jane's family, and her grandfather Doctor Fraser particularly, is helping me in the search.'

The solicitor's expression was strained. 'I suggest you and your friends forget looking for your father, if Joseph is alive and wanted to be found he would have made it easier for you. The whole matter is extremely odd. According to my father who was the Milburn family solicitor before me, your grandmother was always what we called *fey* from a girl and he believed part of that was because she needed to have more of her father's attention.

'You've heard the story about his reaction to his son going against his wishes and vanishing, so I don't need to go into that again but she's getting more of the attention she craves from Leo, her driver. She does get an enormous amount of pleasure from being driven places by him and he seems to know exactly how to handle querulous old women.' Milly told him.

'So, I've been informed. She is very fond of the young man who is her driver, so much so that she has had me draw up a new will to include him. I have urged her not to do anything hasty, but I must do as I am instructed.'

'I understand,' said Milly, standing to leave, then she looked at the solicitor. 'Is there anything else you wish to discuss with me?'

'I'd appreciate it if you could let me have Doctor Fraser's address and telephone number in Northern Ireland. I'd like to ask him a few questions about where his search has led him.'

Milly longed to ask him why he should want to get in touch with the good doctor but decided he would think it was impudent of her, so she remained silent. It was Jane who took a card from her handbag and handed it to the solicitor. He thanked her and saw the two of them out.

–

Jane and Milly spoke little on the way to Jane's house, only pausing for Milly to buy a bunch of flowers for her friend in Clayton Square. When they arrived at the house they were not there long before Kyle and Aunty May arrived. While Jane set the food on the table, Milly poured drinks: a glass of stout for Aunty May, a Guinness for Kyle and glasses of port and lemonade for Jane and Milly. While they ate and drank, Milly and Jane told the other two what the solicitor had discussed with them.

When they had finished, Kyle said, 'I wonder what it is the solicitor wants to know from Doctor Fraser.'

'I wonder if he wants to know how the doctor is getting on with his search?' Milly said.

'That's possible,' said Kyle. 'I'm sure all will end well.'

'I think that depends on what we mean by well,' said Milly. 'When you accompanied me and Mam to Ireland to live with the O'Donnells there, I believed then that it had all ended well. I soon discovered my mistake.'

'We weren't to know that,' he said. 'It was what your mother wanted and if you hadn't gone over there, then she wouldn't have met up again with this bloke she's going to marry.'

She nodded. 'That's true. I just wish I knew the truth about my father.'

Auntie May leaned across the table towards Milly. 'If you're interested in my opinion, I'd stop thinking about your father and accept that if he isn't dead, then his behaviour suggests he took advantage of the confusion in Ireland to reinvent himself and put the past behind him and begin a new life. For all you know he might have another wife and children in another country. He wouldn't be the first person to have married in haste and repented just as swiftly. It's about time the divorce laws in this country were relaxed. Marriages break up over worst things than adultery. Domestic violence being one of them. In the Bible, it says that a man should cherish his wife, not beat her just because his dinner isn't on the table waiting for him when he comes in from work.'

'Are you speaking from personal experience, Auntie May?' Jane asked.

'My sister had a brute of a husband and he would have beaten her to death if I hadn't happened to call on them that evening. They didn't hear me knocking at the front door, so I went in the back and prevented a murder when I caught him giving her terrible thrashing. What did the bobby say? He didn't believe in interfering in domestics and that I shouldn't have hit my brother-in-law with a saucepan. I told him exactly what I thought of him. He threatened to arrest me, so I left and went back later after seeing my brother-in-law go out to the pub. I persuaded my sister to dress the kiddie and to accompany me to my digs. That wasn't the end of it, but at least she and the kiddie survived and went to live in a quiet little village in Wales. As for the husband, he's still in prison after being involved in a drunken brawl during which he stabbed a bloke.'

Kyle stared at her in astonishment. 'How is it you've never told me about this?'

'It was in another city and happened years ago, but it's probably part of the reason why I never married. That and loving showbiz.'

'If my daddy was a violent man, I think I'd have heard of it from the O'Donnells,' said Milly.

'I'm not saying he was violent, chuck, but just that he and your mother mightn't have suited and he took what he considered the easy way out.'

'But that would mean he didn't care about me,' said Milly in a trembling voice.

'I'm sure he did care about you, otherwise he would not have insisted on you returning to England,' said Auntie May. 'But if I remember rightly from what Kyle told me, your father was a sailor which means he saw little of you and most fathers in my opinion leave the rearing of their daughters to the mothers.'

Milly accepted what the older woman said and found herself wondering what if her grandmother had given birth to a daughter, would it have made a difference. She decided to change the subject.

'Did any of you read in the *Echo* about some earl's daughter and her husband disputing a will. A £300,000 fortune is at stake, but apparently there are two wills in existence, and the daughter inheriting any of that fortune was in doubt because the earl believed what his wife told him about his son-in-law beating his daughter. Her Ladyship disliked the son-in-law, so influenced her husband to alter his will and not to leave anything to his daughter, but she insists her mother has been telling lies.'

Kyle gave a low whistle, while Jane said, 'That's a heck of a lot of money.'

'It makes one wonder how the Earl managed to hang on to that amount of money when thousands have lost out on their investments since the Wall Street crash,' said Kyle.

'I read about a sick man having sixpence stolen off him in Walton post office,' said Jane. 'Which puts things into perspective. Anyway, have you the money, Milly, to buy your boat ticket to Dublin?'

'I'm glad to say Mam enclosed a money order in her letter,' said Milly.

'That must be a relief to you,' Kyle said.

Milly nodded. 'Jane said I can stay here for a few days before leaving for Dublin,' she said. 'I was going to ask before I go to Ireland, whether you and Jane have set the date for your wedding yet?'

Kyle glanced at Jane. 'Are we still set on Whit weekend?'

'Yes, I love the month of June and I can't think of any reason to wait longer. We'll need to send out the invitations soon. I don't want a big fuss, but there are people I definitely want there.'

'I hope that includes me,' said Milly.

'And me,' Auntie May said.

'Of course,' said Jane. 'We also need to decide where we're going to live.'

'This is a nicely situated house,' said Auntie May. 'Near a park and a church and some decent shops.'

'And the church has an infant school close by,' added Jane. 'But won't you miss Kyle as a neighbour, Auntie May?'

'I saw the way things were going with you two a while ago,' she said. 'So, I wrote to my sister asking would she be willing to put up with me and explained why. She jumped at the idea. After all, we'll be able to share living expenses, and Wales is beautiful. Her village isn't that far from the sea.'

'So, everything is falling into place for you two,' Milly said. 'Can Jimmy come to the wedding too?'

The happy couple nodded and that made Milly happy. It seemed an age since she had seen Jimmy and she hoped he had missed her as much as she had missed him. She was determined to pop round and see him before she left for Ireland and tell him all her news. She might not have found her father, but for the moment she had other things on her mind.

Chapter Eighteen

March 1931, Belfast

Doctor Fraser put his stethoscope back in his bag. 'Your father is very ill, but if we can see him through the next few days then he'll probably come out alright on the other side, the next few days are critical however.'

'Did you hear that, Pappy?' Eileen Milburn whispered to her father. 'The doctor thinks you're going to get better.'

In the bed, lay a man in his late-sixties and Doctor Fraser, despite the man's poor state of health, couldn't get the notion out of his head that the man reminded him strongly of someone else. He kept his voice low as he spoke to the man's two daughters who were both in the room. 'I'm going to give you a medical prescription for a linctus which you must give to the pharmacist, also give him two aspirins four times a day and keep a cool flannel handy to help with the fever. This is a bad dose of influenza and could kill even a younger, fitter person.'

The man in the bed let out a croak before saying in a weak voice, 'Come here, Addie, I need to speak with you.' Doctor Fraser noticed the unmistakeable Lancashire accent in his voice.

'What is it Pappy? You should be resting, not talking.' The man seemed agitated, so his daughter knelt by the side of his bed to hear him better.

'I need you to go to England and find my sister. I should have sought her out years ago,' he said weakly.

Doctor Fraser could scarcely believe his ears and he now realised that the man in the bed bore a very strong resemblance to Adelaide Martin. Could it be that this was the long-lost brother, here in Belfast and one of his very own patients?

He stepped outside while the daughters listened to their father's request and when they came out, he was writing the prescription. 'Please can you give me your father's full name,' he asked Addie, the elder of the two women.

'Of course, it's Bob Milburn,' she replied.

'Is that his real name?' the doctor asked.

'I'm not sure why you ask, but as it happens, his real first name is Barnaby, but everyone calls him Bob,' she replied.

He paused for a moment before writing this name down on the prescription and handing it to her. 'Is your father by any chance from Lancashire?'

'Yes, he is, he came here from England as a stage performer and never returned once he met Mammy and had us kids. Funnily enough, he just told me that he wants me to find his sister. Before he dies he said. But I have no idea where to start.'

'I believe I can help you there,' Doctor Fraser told her and over a cup of tea in the kitchen, he explained to them both about Adelaide, Milly and the search for Barnaby over in England.

'I've also had a letter from Mrs Martin's solicitor enquiring how the search is going here, and I've certainly got this news to share with him now. I shall write to him immediately and tell him what we have discovered.

I believe that your father is one and the same man that they have been looking for and I believe an inheritance is at stake. I shall also write to my granddaughter, Jane, and she can tell Milly, the young lass who has been looking so hard for your father.'

'This could be just the news that Pappy needs to help with his recovery,' said Addie.

—

Once Doctor Fraser had left, the two sisters spoke about their father's request.

'Are you sure you should be going to England while Dad is so ill?' asked Eileen.

'It's what he wants,' replied Addie. 'You can surely manage him and Midge and Luke? Mrs Fitzpatrick will give you a helping hand if you need it.' Midge was a distant cousin on Addie's mother's side who had been orphaned in her teens and Luke was their younger brother.

'But you could be away for ages. He's set you a difficult task and I'm worried about the next few days.'

'I believe Pappy will pull through and I'll be back for his birthday whatever happens,' promised Addie.

'But what if he gets worse before then?' Eileen asked.

'He won't. Doctor Fraser is going to come back every day he said. Apparently, he's going to get the Liverpool solicitor to pay his fees.'

'What solicitor?' Eileen gnawed at her lower lip.

'The Milburn family solicitor, Mr Lancaster. Apparently, this Mr Lancaster in Liverpool is a descendent from a firm in northern England which has served members of the family over many years.'

Thirty-year-old Addie set her hat at a rakish angle on her jet-black hair and smiled at her sister's reflection in the mirror above the fireplace in the kitchen. Eileen was as fair as Addie was dark, and strangers found it difficult to believe they were sisters.

'What about my job? I can't afford to stay off work and I doubt Midge can cope with Dad when I'm not here,' moaned Eileen.

'I'll speak to Mrs Fitzpatrick before I go and ask her to look in now and again while you're at the mill.' Addie shrugged on her best tweed coat and sighed deeply. 'Let's look on the bright side of things. I'm doing what Dad has wanted to do for some time, but Mammy made a fuss and wouldn't let him. He gave in to her far too much. His giving up the stage really broke him.'

'But surely you can understand why Mammy wanted him at home – what with the fighting and the raids that happen every now and again?' Eileen twisted her hands together and stared glumly at her sister.

Addie nodded. 'Up to a point, although she spent more time with her sisters than with Pappy when he was home. I understand your fears but there's no reason why this house should be raided. We've never taken sides or involved ourselves in politics.'

'I know but the innocent often get up caught in the middle. I mean jobs can be affected and buildings can be set alight. It's not unknown for a mill to be set on fire or a school or a church when tensions between the Catholic and the Protestant factions boil over – we all get caught in the crossfire, sometimes literally.'

'I know, Eileen, but my being here won't change that happening and Dad has set his heart on finding his family in England again. If it is his dying wish, then I know he'd want me to go. Now we know who the family solicitor is, that takes us one step closer. He wants me to visit his sister, so you're just going to have to be alert and steer clear of troublemakers.'

Eileen nodded and squared her shoulders. 'So, after you arrive in Liverpool, you'll speak to the solicitor before seeing Aunt Adelaide?' said Eileen.

'Those are Dad's orders.' Addie picked up the Gladstone bag that had been her father's when he was an impressionist and actor. It was old, having been given to him by his mother and so it had seen a fair amount of travelling, but he had looked after it well. It opened out into two compartments and could carry a lot more in her opinion than a suitcase of a similar size, and just as important, it would be a constant reminder of her father and his mother.

The following day she went to say farewell to her father once again, but he was sleeping after taking the draught that the doctor had prescribed, so she kissed his forehead and crept out of the room thinking he looked a little better. Then she felt terrible about leaving her younger sister and Midge to cope with her father and younger brother Luke, she hugged and kissed them. Addie left the house, not forgetting to drop in next door and ask if their aging neighbour, who was of part-Scottish descent like many in Northern Ireland, could keep an eye on the family whom Addie was leaving behind. Hopefully, to find good news of the family which her father had not seen for so many decades and which was now in her hands to resolve.

-

It was dusk when the ship docked in Liverpool and Addie realised that she would need to find somewhere to stay the night as it was too late to see the solicitor that day. Once she was through customs, Addie was almost overcome by youths offering to carry her bag and accompany her to a supposedly clean and respectable lodging house. She spotted a small boy who was really just a child and who looked timid and apprehensive. His eyes pleaded with her and she handed her bag to him. Several of the bigger lads tried to snatch it from him but he hugged it against his chest and managed to worm his way through the crush. She forced a way through with her elbows and as the pair of them emerged into the open, she freed a sigh. He beamed a smile in her direction.

'My name is Ben, miss, my parents and me and my two older brothers live with my grandmother in the hotel she owns, close to Lime Street station. We all help her out, except for Dad who was injured in the war. I'm sure you'll enjoy your stay with us because it's clean and respectable.'

'That's very interesting, Ben, and a small hotel will suit me fine as I really want somewhere to stay just for a single night's bed and breakfast as I have business in the city.'

Disappointment crossed his appealing boyish features and then he said, 'That's alright, miss.' He paused. 'Am I to understand that you're not here early for the Grand National then? It's so popular one has to get here early to be sure of a bed for the night.'

Addie shook her head. 'I'm here to find my aunt.'

Ben came to a halt as they came out opposite the Liver Building. 'Do you mind a walk, or do you want to take the tram or a cab?'

'As long as the walk isn't too far, I'd enjoy stretching my legs and seeing a bit of Liverpool,' said Addie.

'Dad is Irish the same as you, but he speaks different to you and…' he stopped abruptly, staring at an approaching angry-looking youth.

'Ben, Mam will skin you alive!' said the youth. 'It's Teddy who should be down here, you're too young.'

Addie faced the youth. 'Don't shout at him! He's a perfect little gentleman. I presume you're his brother.'

'Yes, miss. I'm Mick Ryan.'

'Then perhaps you can help Ben with my bag? For all his willingness, I think he's beginning to struggle with it.'

Mick took the bag from Ben who was reluctant to give it up and then Addie said softly, 'Ben, let your brother help you. That's what families are for.'

Ben surrendered the bag to Mick with a sigh. 'I wish I was older,' he said.

'Don't be wishing your life away, Ben,' Addie said. 'Enjoy being young while you can.'

'She said she'll be happy to walk,' said Ben to his brother with a hop, skip and a jump.

'Who's 'she'? The cat's mother?' said Mick. 'Apologies for my little brother's coarseness, what is your name, miss?'

Addie smiled. 'Miss Milburn. Miss Adelaide Milburn.'

'You're from the north of Ireland,' Mick said. 'Belfast?'

Addie nodded. 'Now can we be on our way? I'm hungry. Is it possible your mammy can provide me with supper?'

Mick nodded. 'And she's a good cook is Ma.' He decided to take Miss Milburn up towards the Victoria Monument and along Church Street, so she could see the shops and then past Saint Peter's church before turning into Ranelagh Street, past Lewis's department store, then all the way up to Mount Pleasant where the Arcadia was situated.

As they strolled along, Addie found herself wishing she could stay longer in Liverpool and had more money in her purse, so she could buy her family something special as a souvenir of her visit to the city.

She received a warm welcome from the old lady in reception, Mrs Neilson, a widow who was the owner of the establishment. She showed Addie up to a bedroom on the second floor overlooking the cobbled road below. The window reached almost from the ceiling to the floor, and the gaslight glowed warmly off the well-polished dressing table and small wardrobe. Mick followed in their wake with Addie's bag.

'Michael, fetch a jug of hot water up for Miss Milburn, please,' said Mrs Neilson, before turning to Addie. 'And my daughter, Kitty, will have a supper ready for you within the hour.'

'Thank you,' said Addie.

As soon as they had left, Addie sat on one of the twin beds and bounced up and down and was satisfied, thinking she would sleep well that night. She hung up her coat in the wardrobe and removed a nightdress and a light jumper and skirt from her bag, as well as a clean pair of cami-knickers, a flannel and a sliver of soap in a tin. Then to her delight and amazement she discovered a small unopened block of Lux soap in a dish on the washstand. Such soap was considered a luxury back at home in Ireland where there wasn't much money for extras, and they had to make do with a block of carbolic. To discover it available for a use in this hotel room said much to her of the owner's determination to please her guests.

At that moment, there was a knock at the bedroom door and a voice she recognised as Mick's said, 'Your hot water, Miss Milburn. I'll leave it outside the door for you.'

She thanked him and as she heard his footsteps retreating, she went and fetched the water. As she did so the door opposite opened and a young woman came out. She smiled at Addie. 'You've only just arrived,' she said with a faint Scottish accent.

Addie said, 'Yes, nice hotel, isn't it?'

The woman nodded. 'And reasonable rates considering there's racing at Aintree this month. My husband and I are staying until after the National on the 25th or 26th then we're going over to the Wirral to stay with relatives in Eastham for a few days and then to London to see another cousin and her husband. They had a baby last December and I've yet to see the wee bairn.'

'I'm over from Belfast to look up an aunt whom I've never met.'

'I hope you find her well and enjoy your visit,' she held out a hand and introduced herself. 'I'm Mrs Fiona Murray from Edinburgh.'

'Miss Adelaide Milburn from Belfast,' said Addie. 'I wish you luck at the races and that you have an enjoyable visit with your relatives.'

'Thanks.'

They went downstairs together, parting in reception as Fiona's husband came out of the smoking room, pipe in hand. They left the hotel and Addie went into the dining room where a small table was set ready for her. Within minutes of her sitting down, a bowl of mushroom soup with some thick slices of bread and butter was set before her and her water glass was filled from a jug with lemon slices floating in the water.

She thanked Mick, who was acting as waiter before leaving her to her meal. The soup was delicious, flavoursome and creamy. As she ate, her thoughts strayed to the family she had left behind, and she prayed that her father's health would improve, that Eileen and Midge would manage without her, and her younger brother Luke would behave himself until she returned home. Since her mother had died a good few years ago now of tuberculosis, Addie had taken on the reins of the household while attending night school to learn to type and do shorthand, while also maintaining a job as a lowly clerk in the office of a linen mill. Unfortunately, when her father had taken ill, she had to give up her job, much to the displeasure of her boss who told her, 'I rely on you, Miss Milburn. You having worked here so long means you know all there is to know about the business.'

Addie had felt terrible letting him down, especially as she liked him, and she thought he liked her too. They worked well together and yet she knew he would have to find someone else to take her place. Most likely it would be Nora Sullivan who had been her rival for the position years ago and Addie knew she would never manage to get a job she enjoyed so much again or with a boss who was so nice to her. No doubt she would end up as an old maid, poor and lonely with only a cat to keep her company as she was not pretty like Eileen, nor appealing like Midge. Fortunately, she had managed to save some of her wages for the rainy days her mother used to go on about.

When her father had suggested Addie go to England to see his twin sister, she fell in with his wishes, thinking at first that he only wanted to be in touch with his sister before he died, because even if he recovered from his present illness, he couldn't have much longer to live.

She finished her soup and set the bowl to one side as the dining room door opened and Mick entered, apologising as he set a plate of sandwiches in front of her. 'Ma said that she hoped sandwiches would be alright as there was none of the main meal left?'

'Sandwiches will be fine,' said Addie. 'If I could have a pot of tea with them that would be grand.'

Micky smiled. 'I'll tell Ma. I'll be back with it in a jiffy.'

He was as good as his word and soon Addie was relaxing with a cup of tea and the plate of egg and cress sandwiches, and when they were finished, she turned in for the night.

The next morning, she was up early and went down to breakfast as soon as the gong sounded. She ate heartily of a plate of toast, bacon and egg and drank two cups of tea before packing her few items of clothing and toiletries in her small overnight bag. Then she went downstairs and paid her bill and asked could they hold on to her Gladstone bag in case she did not stay at her aunt's. She would let them know her plans as soon as possible. She was joined a short while later by Mick who led the way out of the hotel. She told him she needed to go to Castle Street.

Addie enjoyed the walk and hearing that Liverpool had once had its own castle, hence the street name. On arrival at the solicitor's address, she thanked Mick for his help and gave him a tip. She gazed at the highly polished brass plates on the soot-darkened wall and saw that the solicitor was on the second floor, so she went inside the building and climbed the stairs. She knocked on the door that was partially glazed with the solicitor's name Mr Wilfred Lancaster written there in gold-coloured lettering.

A few minutes passed and then the door opened to reveal a young woman in a grey costume with a pale-blue

229

blouse fastened at the neck with a bow. 'May I help you?' she asked.

'I hope so,' Addie said with a smile. 'I'm Miss Adelaide Milburn and I am searching for my father's sister, Mrs Adelaide Martin. I believe I am expected.'

'Ahh! You're the Irish niece of Mrs Adelaide Martin. You've caused quite a bit of excitement! Do come in, my dear. You will have to wait a short while as Mr Lancaster has a client with him.'

A quarter of an hour later the door to Mr Lancaster's private office opened and a middle-aged woman with a fox fur draped about her shoulders emerged. She nodded briefly in the secretary's direction, and left. The secretary waited a few moments before knocking on the door of Mr Lancaster's private office, she was called inside, and a couple of minutes later she called Addie in, holding the door open for her to enter.

Quelling the butterflies in her tummy, Addie entered the room and stared at the man who had stood to greet her as she entered. He was balding and had a round, chubby face that revealed dimples in his cheek as he broke into a smile. He stretched forth a hand across the sturdy desk of oak and said, 'It's a pleasure to meet you, Miss Milburn. I only wish Doctor Fraser had encountered your father earlier. We've been looking for him for a long time. Please sit down.'

She took his hand and shook it, glad that his handshake was firm and not clammy, then she took a seat opposite Mr Lancaster.

The solicitor spent a long time explaining to Addie about the long search for her father and Adelaide Martin's unshakeable belief that he was still alive. He also explained about the inheritance passed down from Barnaby's parents.

'Your grandmother stated in her will that a certain sum of money was to be set aside for your father if he were traced by your father's fiftieth birthday date. If he was not found by that date, then the money would go to his twin, Adelaide.'

'Does the delay mean we won't be inheriting any money,' sighed Addie.

'I didn't say that. Fortunately, your grandmother added a codicil that if it was discovered at a later date that he had children of his own, they would inherit the amount meant for him.'

'Does my pappy know about the codicil?' she asked.

'Doctor Fraser wrote to me as soon as he learnt your father's identity and I have informed Mr Milburn of the situation by post today.'

Addie's face flushed. 'I don't think he cares about the money for himself at all. He's ill, which is why I am here. At least he swallowed his stupid pride eventually.'

'Do you have a photograph of him with you?' Mr Lancaster asked her.

'Aye, I do.'

She pulled open her coat and had a rummage around in the inside pocket before finding what she was looking for in a brown envelope. She handed it over to the solicitor who opened it and smiled at the photograph.

'Well, this is more like it! The man in this photograph bears a strong resemblance to Adelaide Martin.'

'Of course, he does, they're twins, what would you expect,' she said, her eyes raised in surprise.

Mr Lancaster gave a wry laugh. 'You might be surprised when I tell you that your father is not the only person who has come forward in this matter.' Addie looked perplexed, so Mr Lancaster said, '…all will become clear in due course, my dear.'

'Does my aunt know about this yet?' she asked him.

'I have not told your aunt her twin has been found but I'm sure she will be delighted to see you.'

'Has she any children?' asked Addie.

'Adelaide is a widow, she had a son Joseph who married an Irish girl and a granddaughter Milly.' He hesitated before continuing, 'Sadly, the elder Mr Martin died when Joseph was quite young. The boy's mother became overly protective and possessive, so it was not surprising that Joseph went to sea.'

'Poor Aunt Adelaide! It definitely doesn't pay to love someone too much.' She hesitated before adding, 'What about Joseph's wife and daughter?'

'Bridget, his wife and Milly, his daughter, lived with your aunt, but there was a lot of discord between the two women. I think it would be best if you heard the rest of the story from Milly. Right now, she is still here in Liverpool but will shortly be going to Dublin, I understand from Doctor Fraser. She is young woman of seventeen or eighteen.'

'I'd like to meet her. The big question is will she resent me?'

'I doubt it,' he said comfortingly. 'I shall come with you to see her and explain everything. Besides, I have more news for her.'

Chapter Nineteen

Addie stood next to Mr Lancaster outside the terraced house where he had been told by Doctor Fraser that Milly was staying with her friend. He had attempted to call ahead to let them know they were coming but the exchange told him there was no telephone listed at that address. Addie was attempting to keep her apprehension and excitement under control as he raised his arm and banged the door knocker loudly.

She waited impatiently, aware that a net curtain in the bay window to her right had been raised and a woman was peering out at her. Then the curtain dropped and a few moments later the door opened, and a pretty girl with red, wavy hair in the modern style stood there.

'Mr Lancaster, can I help you, who's this?' she asked looking at Addie directly.

Mr Lancaster nudged her elbow gently. 'Tell her who you are, my dear.'

'Well, who are you?' Milly asked again.

Addie took a deep breath before saying, in as confident a voice as she could muster, 'My name is Adelaide Milburn. My father is Barnaby Milburn and this solicitor, Mr Lancaster, has brought me here. If you are Milly Martin, he thinks you and I should be better acquainted.'

The girl gasped. 'I'm Milly. This is a right turn up for the books,' she paused. 'You'd best come in both of you.

This is the home of my friend, Miss Jane Fraser who I'm staying with.'

Addie and Mr Lancaster followed Milly inside and up a lobby to a rear room where a woman who appeared to be of a similar age to Addie herself was sitting, knitting. She set her knitting to one side and stood up as Milly said, 'Jane, this is my great-uncle Barnaby's daughter, Adelaide Milburn. Mr Lancaster has brought her to meet me.'

'How exciting,' said Jane, stretching out a hand with a surprised look on her face. 'I presume you'll tell us how this came about. Do sit down, Miss Milburn and Mr Lancaster.' She waved them towards two chairs close to the fire. 'Cup of tea?'

'Unfortunately, I can't stop for long, ladies. I have come specifically with some very interesting news.' Mr Lancaster said as he sat himself down at the kitchen table and bid Milly sit next to him. 'Do you remember the letter I had regarding the imposter I believe to have been pretending to be Mr Barnaby?'

'Yes,' said Milly. 'You were looking for more proof.'

'I was and I have found it. It is possible to obtain copies of birth, marriage and death records from Somerset House in London, you could attend in person, but you do have to fill in relevant paperwork to do so. I have a contact there and I was able to obtain information about the person who requested this birth certificate and they have sent me a copy of the application.'

He took a carbon copy of a piece of paperwork out from his briefcase and pushed it towards her. 'Do you recognise the name of the applicant?'

Milly picked it up to view it and her mouth opened in shock. 'The name is Liam O'Donnell!'

'Is he someone you know?' Mr Lancaster asked.

'Yes, more's the pity. He's one of the Liverpool O'Donnell clan,' she answered.

'But why would he pretend to be my pappy?' Addie wondered aloud.

'Your mother's divorce changes everything for the O'Donnell side of the family,' Mr Lancaster told them. 'The only way the O'Donnells would obtain any inheritance now would be through fraud or theft.'

'He must have heard all about Barnaby Milburn and the inheritance through Mammy's cousin, Brendon, and decided to try his luck,' said Milly, 'but I wonder who the man in the photograph was?'

'I'm sure we'll get to the bottom of it eventually. Fraud is a very serious crime and I intend to report this to the police. Now, I have much pressing business to attend to and bid you good day.'

'Well, that's another turn up for the books,' Milly said after he had left, and they were seated around the fire.

'I always knew Liam was up to no good,' Jane agreed.

'He must have had help. He's not clever enough to do something like that himself,' Milly stated.

Addie said, 'But do tell me if you will, Milly, your story and what happened to you and your family. Mr Lancaster thought it best if I heard your story from you.'

Jane said, 'I'll make a pot of tea while you two talk.'

Milly drew a dining chair close to the armchair where Addie was sitting, and it wasn't long before Jane poured them all another tea from the big brown teapot. Milly told Jane the now familiar tale of her upbringing.

'Am I right to believe that Mr Lancaster told you my mother and I had been living with my grandmother, that she and my mother had a row and so Mammy flounced out with me, saying she'd had enough of Grandma's interference and insults?'

'He didn't tell me what was said...' put in Addie as Milly paused for breath.

'They were always arguing, with me being piggy in the middle,' said Milly. 'Grandma wanted me to carry on living with her and for Mammy to leave but Mammy wasn't having any of that despite us having little in the way of money. Mammy decided we would find somewhere else to live and she would get a job.'

Addie gasped. 'Your mother must have been off her trolley, not to return to Aunt Adelaide's house.'

'No, she was just as stubborn as Grandma and eventually she found herself a job working in a Chinese laundry, ironing sheets and shirts and the like. The owner took a fancy to her and offered us lodgings with him and his mother.'

'That's quite a story,' said Addie. 'So where was your daddy all this time?'

Milly told her of the story of the continued search for him. 'I'd have thought Mr Lancaster might have told you all that.'

'He might have but I had so much information to assimilate that it must have slipped me by. So, what happened next?'

Milly raced through the next part of her story about Mr Chin and then her rescue by Anne and Andrew before bringing everything up to date.

A fascinated Addie couldn't take her eyes from Milly's face. She was completely unaware of her tea going cold and Jane pouring her a fresh cup. 'So, your mother is having a divorce through abandonment and is marrying again. Aunt Adelaide must have mixed feelings about that.' She took a sip of tea.

'I honestly believe she doesn't care about Mammy remarrying and is probably glad to have the connection with her broken. This way it keeps alive the hope of Daddy being around. What she hates is my agreeing to be Mam's bridesmaid.'

'Perhaps she thinks it disloyal of you to your father's memory,' said Addie with feeling.

'Maybe,' mused Milly. 'But I owe Mammy a certain loyalty. And…' she added vexedly, '…if Daddy were alive still, he should have been in touch with us if he really cared about us.' Milly was annoyed that this second cousin should presume to judge the situation so quickly.

'But what if he really has lost his memory?' asked Addie.

'He must have begun a new life,' said Milly firmly.

'So, does that mean you are no longer interested in finding him?'

'It means I've stopped believing in Grandma's vision of seeing him alive. I feel I have wasted too much of my life on a quest that I put my heart and soul into, searching for a father whom I scarcely knew and who apparently risked his life for a cause that wasn't his. I've come to the conclusion that he must have wanted Mam and me out of the way, so he could pursue his own ends.'

'It does seem odd,' Addie said. 'I mean my dad was often away but we knew he'd turn up eventually.'

Milly said, 'Why didn't he get in touch with his sister?'

Addie glanced at her. 'He had a life in Ireland and my mammy didn't want her interfering, so he said.'

'Then why is he making contact now?' asked Milly. 'Although, maybe I don't need to ask. Money!'

Addie flushed with annoyance. 'Because he's ill and has been wanting to find his sister for some time, my mammy who passed away always put a stop to it. Perhaps she was afraid Pappy would leave us and come back to England. Jane, it was your grandfather who made the connection and helped us to find Mr Lancaster. It was he who told me about the will when I got here, we knew nothing of it.'

'Good old grandfather, so his investigations came good?' Jane commented.

'I think it was a bit of luck too, Pappy just happened to be one of his patients, would you believe.'

'Fancy that!' Jane exclaimed. 'It's like fate.'

'Mr Lancaster told me about Pappy's mother's will. If he was found by a certain date, then he inherited a sum of money which was set aside for him.'

'What if he wasn't found?' asked Jane.

'It went to Adelaide.' Addie gulped. 'Dad is ill, he not only wanted to see Aunt Adelaide before he passed away, but he'll want the money due to him for me, my sister and brother before he goes, we don't have much.'

'I'm sorry to hear he's not well,' said Milly, feeling that Addie was in a difficult position, coming into the complicated Milburn and Martin family situation. 'How serious is his illness?'

'Pretty bad, we couldn't afford regular visits from a doctor, but now Doctor Fraser will be paid for by Mr Lancaster, so we've our fingers crossed.'

'Would you like me to go with you to Grandma's house?' Milly asked.

'If you're all right with that?' said Addie, smiling.

'Do you have a photograph of him?' Milly asked and Addie nodded. 'Then that should please her no end.' Milly fetched her coat and hat.

'He's canny is Dad even if he's stiff-necked with pride,' Addie said.

The girls wasted no more time and left the house after putting on their hats and coats.

They were silent as they walked to the main road and it was not until they were on a tram heading into town that Milly thought of asking Addie where she was staying.

'In a hotel on Mount Pleasant,' she replied. 'I only booked for one night, thinking that Aunt Adelaide would ask me to stay with her. My luggage is still there.'

'She probably will ask as long as she doesn't get a cob on. She does get into moods,' said Milly. 'So, tell me do you have a job in Ireland?'

Addie nodded. 'I work in the office of a linen mill.'

'So, you've had an education?'

Addie looked surprised. 'Of sorts.'

'Do you type and know shorthand?'

Addie said, 'Sure I do. Dad was set on it and Mam fell in with his wishes, regardless of the times he was away from home. He was a lot older than her when they married after many years on the road as a performer. He thinks girls should be educated as well as boys. He said his mother was a clever woman, but her father was a real Victorian and didn't believe women's brains were equal to a man's.'

'One can guess what he'd have thought of women's emancipation,' said Milly. 'She'd be my great-grandmother,' she added.

'But my grandmother,' Addie said. 'And your father would be my first cousin. I wish I'd met him.'

'Perhaps that day might come yet,' said Milly, a catch in her throat.

'You mean he could still be alive – and if so, what then?'

Milly shrugged, glancing out of the window. 'We'll be getting off soon.' She stood up and so did Addie, leading the way to the platform of the tram. No sooner had they left the tram in Dale Street, Milly linked her arm through Addie's and urged her up to Exchange Station.

As they left the train, Addie said, 'Why is this place called Waterloo?'

'In commemoration of the battle in which Wellington's troops defeated Napoleon's. You'll find throughout the country, churches that are called Waterloo churches built in commemoration and thanksgiving for the victory.'

'Fancy that,' murmured Addie. 'One learns something new all the time.'

'There's one in Burscough not far from where your dad and Aunt Adelaide lived when they were children.'

'Did you know that Wellington was born in Ireland?' asked Addie.

Milly nodded. 'Regardless of what Grandmother Martin thinks, a lot of heroes and good people are Irish too.'

'Doesn't she like the Irish? The writer of "There is a Green Hill Far Away" was Irish and still an Anglican,' mused Addie. 'Perhaps it's just as well Mam passed away a few years ago. She and Dad made a mixed marriage.'

'So did my parents. I did wonder about your mam,' said Milly. 'I wouldn't let grandmother's prejudice worry you. After all you are half-English and half-Proddie. Even so the rivalry between the Orange and Green is strong in Liverpool.'

'But they don't kill each other?' said Addie with a shudder.

'Sometimes things get out of hand,' Milly said. 'Stones get thrown and there are the odd fights on the twelfth of July. Andrew's father was killed in such a way by accident, but most of the time they rub along fairly amicably.'

'Mine were married in a Catholic church.'

'Mine were wed in a C of E.' Milly paused. 'And you don't have to tell me that some in the Roman Catholic church would say that was no real marriage and that I'm illegitimate. It's enough for me that the marriage was lawful.' She had just finished saying that when they arrived at the entrance to her grandmother's drive.

'Gosh, it's some size,' said Addie on catching sight of the house.

As they drew closer, Leo appeared, coming from the side of the house. He stopped and waved at them. Milly waved back and at the same time told Addie in as few words as possible who he was and of her grandmother's fondness for him.

It was not until he drew closer did Addie realise just how good-looking the young man was, and she wondered if he was a gigolo out to get as much as he could from his employer. As they approached him, she heard Leo telling Milly that he was on his way to see her grandmother to ask what her orders were for him that day.

Milly suggested she might not want to drive out that day as her niece from Ireland had come to visit her. Leo glanced at Addie with a startled expression on his face. Then he suggested that Mrs Martin might ask the young lady to accompany her. The thought had not occurred to Milly, but she realised that it was very much a possibility.

The front door was ajar, so Milly led Addie indoors. Leo followed them a few minutes later, only to bump into Susan.

'What are you doing coming in that way?' she asked.

'I'm just saving time,' he replied. 'Besides which, the mistress doesn't mind my using the front door. Also, Miss Milly is back with a visitor,' he added with a grin.

'Who?' Susan asked.

'The mistress's niece from Ireland.'

Susan's mouth fell open. 'Who?'

'You heard me!'

'But she doesn't have a niece.' Susan nibbled her lower lip.

'Miss Milly says she does.'

As Milly and Addie made their way to the sitting room followed by Leo, Susan wasted no time heading for the kitchen where she made a pot of tea and prepared a tray, before carrying it to the sitting room.

'Place the tray on the table in front of the sofa, Susan,' said Adelaide. 'Milly, you can pour. Who is this woman you have brought with you?'

'I'm glad you are sitting down, Grandma,' Milly said as she arranged the tea things, 'for I've brought this lady here to see you and it might come as a bit of a shock, but it's good news, I promise you.'

Milly bid Addie sit down next to Adelaide on the sofa. Adelaide regarded the woman and Milly could see the old lady's hand shake, and she remembered that her grandmother was old and frail.

'Who is this woman, Mildred?' Her grandmother asked, a little impatiently.

'You tell her, Addie,' Milly said encouragingly.

'My name is Adelaide, like yourself, and my surname is Milburn,' Addie said. Her older namesake looked confused, turning her head from Milly to Addie in a questioning way. 'My father is called Barnaby and he is your brother. Doctor Fraser treated my father, who is ill in Belfast and made the connection between us all. I'm your niece.'

For a moment Milly's grandmother still looked confused, but then asked, 'Is your father alive?'

'He is,' Addie said. 'Doctor Fraser is treating him for the flu, he's old now and a bit frail, but as long as it doesn't turn to pneumonia, he'll be alright, we hope.'

Suddenly Adelaide's features lit up and a smile spread across her face. 'Thanks be to God, I knew he was alive all of this time. Now come my dear, you must tell me everything.'

For the next half-hour or so, Milly listened while Addie told her aunt what she knew of her father stowing away on a ship and leaving it at Dun Laoghaire, then joining a travelling group of entertainers in Dublin and meeting her mother on his travels in Belfast and getting married. He had carried on in the entertaining business while her mother had stayed at home in Belfast with their two daughters and younger son. Adelaide explained about her visions and the search. Both Susan and Leo listened in and eventually Adelaide spoke to her driver.

'Leo, if you'd bring the car round to the front, so it's ready.'

'Where are we going?' Milly asked.

'Not you, dear,' said her grandmother. 'Not this time. I'd like to talk to Adelaide alone.'

Addie frowned, but Milly only said, 'That's all right by me. I've matters to attend to before going to Ireland.'

'I hope you aren't trying to provoke me, Milly?' said her grandmother.

'Not at all,' said Milly disappointed that her grandmother didn't seem to have forgotten her annoyance at her mother's wedding, even though she'd had the news she was waiting for about her brother. 'I'm interested to know where you're taking Addie.'

'Her name is Adelaide,' said her grandmother. 'I'm going to take her out on a drive in the car, so we can talk in private.'

'What about taking me to see your old home where you and Dad lived when you were children?' asked Addie.

'Now there's a thought,' said her aunt, casting a glance at Milly. 'Why have you never suggested seeing the old place?'

'Because my daddy never lived there,' replied Milly, reaching for her handbag. 'Anyway, I'd better be going. I hope the two of you have a lovely day.'

'See you soon, I hope,' said Addie.

'I hope so too,' Milly said.

She kissed her grandmother's cheek and left the house, wondering if her place in her grandmother's life had been well and truly taken over.

Chapter Twenty

Addie said, 'It's a pity Milly couldn't come with us.'

'I'd rather have you to myself,' said Adelaide. 'Did Milly tell you why she's going to Ireland?'

Addie nodded. 'Her mother is remarrying.'

'Did she tell you that she's now divorced from my son?'

'It's a difficult situation for a wife to be in.' Addie topped up their cups of tea. 'I know it was rough on Mother and us kids with Dad being a travelling player on the stage and away a lot.'

'Did Barnaby make a decent living?' asked Adelaide.

'I believe he was very successful for quite a time and then the competition from the up and coming youngsters made it difficult for him to get enough bookings.'

'So how did your family manage?'

'Mother had a job at the mill, and I was old enough to do some training and I gained employment in the mill office,' said Addie. 'Mother died a few years ago, but I kept on with work because my job in the office paid more than my sister Eileen would have earned on the looms full-time, so now she keeps house and works only part-time at the mill. She's there at home for our brother Luke when he finishes school, as well as keeping an eye on Dad's needs with him being older and ill. The rest of the day, a neighbour looks in on him.'

'He should have been in touch,' said Adelaide vexed. 'I would have helped him, after all he named you after me.'

'Dad didn't want to be a burden on you. Besides which he'd heard you'd married. He still cares about you. It was Dad who insisted I come and look you up. He'd like to see you before he passes over. I had to give up my job to come here.'

'Y-you mean he wants me to go to Ireland to see him?' stammered Adelaide.

'To Belfast – if he was fit enough to travel, he would have come here instead of me,' Addie responded quickly.

'But isn't there fighting, and buildings being blown up over there? It would be dangerous, and I could get hurt.'

'There have been riots, due to the Depression making conditions in the city worse for the poor, but if you care about your twin brother, then surely it's a risk you're prepared to take, there's no real danger to a visitor in Belfast,' said Addie.

'I'm an old woman,' said Adelaide in a quavering voice.

Addie stood up. 'I am aware how old you are, the same age as Dad, and that soon you'll both have a birthday. I've promised my sister I'll be back for Dad's birthday. So, if you want to see your brother for one last time, then you need to pluck up your courage, and make up your mind swiftly.'

Adelaide flushed. 'You're very dictatorial and impudent for your age, young woman. Milly would never speak to me in such a way.'

'I don't believe you, she has guts. She already knows you will cut her off without a penny in favour of Leo if she goes to her mother's wedding, but she's still going to go because her mother wants her, and she loves her mother. No doubt you favour Leo because he makes a good substitute for the son who left you to follow his own star, just as my father did. You're prepared to put him before your granddaughter because you see in her another family member who's prepared to go her own way and desert you.'

'You'll regret speaking to me in such a manner, young lady,' spluttered Adelaide.

'Perhaps, because Dad really would like to see you, and I've let my temper get the better of me, but today has aroused strong feelings in all of us.' Addie sighed. 'I'm sorry.'

Her aunt took a deep breath. 'I'm sorry too, I'm better at talking than listening as I've got older.'

Before they could continue, there was a knock and Leo called out that the car was ready. 'We'll be right there,' replied Adelaide.

'You still want me to go with you?' said Addie.

'Of course.' They put on their outdoor hats and coats and made their way to the car. 'You'll be able to tell your father that the old place has changed,' Adelaide said.

'In what way?' Addie asked.

'Susan's mother told me it's a charitable holiday retreat for poor families from the city,' said Leo, glancing their way. 'A mission worth supporting.'

'What a good idea!' Addie exclaimed.

'As long as they have the right staff,' he said, opening the front passenger seat for his employer. 'I'll need you to direct me, madam,' he said.

Adelaide smiled. 'At least I'm good for something,' she said. 'That's if I remember the way. Perhaps we should take Susan with us.'

'Should I go and fetch her?' Leo asked.

Addie opened the rear passenger door behind her aunt and waited to hear her answer before sliding along the seat.

'Why not? A day in the country where she can see her mother would be good for her,' said Adelaide, surprising Addie.

Ten minutes or so later, a breathless Susan and Leo arrived at the car. Adelaide stepped out of the car and moved into the back with Addie, while Susan sat in the front after thanking her employer for the unexpected treat.

Soon they were on their way and although Susan had never travelled to the village where her mother lived by car, she had once been given a lift by horse and cart, so she remembered signposts and some landmarks on the way and suggested they headed for Southport first before turning right towards Ormskirk.

Within less than two hours, they had arrived in Burscough and she indicated to Leo which direction to take to Adelaide's childhood home. She suggested Leo drive up to the house, which was in the Georgian style, because she was convinced that when her employer introduced herself and explained the house had once been her home that they were bound to be welcomed into the building.

It was just as Susan thought and in no time at all Addie was in a daze as she recognised places that her father had spoken about over the years. After leaving the house and strolling around the grounds, her aunt brought to life the horse chestnut tree which her father had climbed as a dare, and the den that they had made with some local children in the centre of a rhododendron bush, as well as the stream where they had paddled and fished for tiddlers.

'Happy days,' said Adelaide.

'I'm sure Dad would enjoy coming here with you, Aunt Adelaide, and reliving old times,' Addie said.

'Hopefully, he will get better and be able to come,' said Adelaide, a catch in her throat. 'I remember coming here with my husband and Joseph and both said, I was a lucky duck to have grown up here.' She sighed. 'I remember holidays to Blackpool, Morecambe, the Lake District, even to the Isle of Man – a ferry sailed from Heysham. A ferry also goes from there to Ireland.'

'I think Dad sailed from Heysham,' said Addie.

Addie was amazed by the change in her aunt, wondering how different she might have been if her menfolk had not left her behind when they went adventuring, but that had been the way of the opposite sex in days gone, considering women the weaker sex.

Thank God for women's emancipation this century, she thought.

Lady Hester Stanhope set the standard when she went travelling on her own to the Holy Land during the last century; however, women still had a very long way to go now to have equal rights with men. Even in the mill where she worked, women were paid less than men for doing the same job. Still, part of her wished her father had stayed behind here, because surely, he would have been the heir to this house and land and then she and her siblings would have grown up here. But if he hadn't run off to Ireland, most likely he wouldn't have met her mother, and then Eileen, Luke and herself wouldn't have been born or become the people they were today.

As she watched some children chasing each other in the grounds of the house, she thought how much better it was that poorer children had the chance and pleasure of being here instead. That caused her to remember what Leo had said about the right staff being important and wondered about his background and where he had come from. It was then that she realised that she had not caught sight of him for a while, neither had she seen Susan. Then she recalled that the housekeeper's mother lived in the village and concluded that he might have escorted her there and aimed on having a look around the village at the same time.

It was to be some time before she caught sight of Leo again and he was talking to one of the guardians of the retreat centre. She pointed him out to her aunt and asked whether she needed him to fetch the picnic hamper from the car.

'Now there's an idea. I am starting to feel hungry,' said Adelaide. 'Do go and tell him, there's a dear. We'll go and sit by the stream where there's a bench. He can find us there.'

Addie did so and once she and her aunt were seated on the bench, she asked her where Leo had previously worked and whether he had family. 'He was brought up in an orphanage further up north,' replied her aunt. 'As it happens, the Millburn's have their roots in the border country too.'

'I think Dad told me that they were border reivers in olden times and was surprisingly proud of the fact, considering they were cattle raiders.'

'The Scots were also reivers, so it was a case of tit for tat,' said Adelaide who watched greedily as Leo unpacked the hamper, spreading a cloth on the bench between the two women. He poured out chilled homemade lemonade from a thermos flask into beakers.

'Have you had anything to eat?' she asked.

'I had a bite at Susan's mother's,' he replied. 'She's a kindly soul. Getting on a bit now and that gives Susan cause to worry, although the neighbours are helpful.'

'I suppose it's the rheumatics,' said Adelaide. 'Her cottage is picturesque but damp, I imagine. I offered her a job working for me, but she turned it down, saying she was too old.'

'So, what's Susan going to do?' asked Addie.

He took a deep breath. 'We've been discussing that with her mother just now and she was telling us that the retreat is advertising for more staff, so we've decided to apply for two of the positions, so we can be near her mother.'

'I don't understand,' said Adelaide, her voice trembling. 'You both have good jobs with me. Why should you want to live up here?'

'Susan and I love each other, and we want to get married.'

Addie stared at her aunt and could see that such an event had never occurred to her.

'But I've been generous to you,' said Adelaide. 'And as for Susan, well, she's been with me for years.'

'All the more reason to feel like a change, Aunt,' said Addie.

'Keep out of this, niece,' flashed her aunt, sending her a fierce look. 'You've only been here five minutes and you think you know it all.'

'The outsider often sees things that others can't,' Addie said.

Adelaide turned on Leo and said, 'I expect you to serve a month's notice and the same with Susan. Now clear the picnic away and place the hamper in the boot.'

He inclined his head and said, 'Yes, madam.'

As soon as he was out of earshot, Adelaide said, 'Servants aren't what they used to be.'

'I wouldn't know,' said Addie. 'I've never been a servant or hired one.'

'Well, we can change that,' Adelaide said. 'You can visit the servants' employment bureau and arrange for a housekeeper-cum-cook and a chauffeur to come for an interview.'

'I haven't come here to be your servant,' said Addie.

Adelaide stared at her fixedly. 'You're being impudent. I'll have words with Barnaby when I see him about your manners.'

'So, you are going to make the effort to visit him?' Addie could not disguise her astonishment.

'I never said I wouldn't,' muttered her aunt. 'Now help me up and give me your arm to assist me to the car.'

'You should say please,' said Addie, hoisting her aunt to her feet.

'Don't push your luck,' retorted Adelaide. 'Just because Leo, Susan and Milly are being removed from my will. It doesn't say I'll put you in their places.'

'I don't care,' Addie said casually. 'I know that Dad was mentioned in his mother's will and his legacy has been in a trust all these years.'

'Who told you that?' Adelaide's face went pale beneath her face powder.

'Mr Lancaster, the solicitor. Doctor Fraser suggested I visit him.'

For a moment Addie thought her aunt was going to have a fit of apoplexy and so, she put her arm around her waist and told her to lean on her, but the older woman ignored her suggestion and stood still, taking several deep breaths before walking on. Addie walked behind her.

Chapter Twenty-one

When they arrived back at where the car was parked, Addie suggested that Leo drive them to Susan's mother's cottage where Susan could make a pot of tea and put a shot of brandy in it as his mistress had suffered a shock.

After he had parked outside the cottage, Adelaide accepted a cup of tea, doctored with brandy, with scarcely any comment, and refused to get out of the car and enter the cottage. She slept most of the way home, only waking when she heard the roar of the waves on Waterloo shore which indicated that the wind had risen. She shivered and told Addie she was imagining what it would be like to be halfway across the Irish Sea if she were to go to Belfast. When they arrived at the house, she needed assistance climbing out of the car and was so unsteady on her feet that Leo lifted her and carried her upstairs to her bedroom with Susan leading the way, and Addie following behind. He left the two women to put her to bed and then went downstairs and put the kettle on and filled a hot-water bottle. He took it upstairs while Addie called Doctor Fraser's surgery in Belfast and brought him up to date with what was happening and asked could he inform her father and sister. Susan put the hot-water bottle in her mistress's bed and made her as comfortable as possible.

'Do you think she's going to be all right?' asked Addie.

Susan nodded. 'She's as tough as old boots physically, but mentally and emotionally she's a wreck. I feel sorry for her, but I've had enough of putting my own life on the back burner, and I must put my own mam first.'

'Understandable,' said Addie.

'Will you be staying here long?' Susan asked.

'Adelaide told me that she wants me to stay with her as I was settling her upstairs, so I'll be here a month,' replied Addie. 'Then I must return to Belfast, I promised to be home for Dad's birthday. Hopefully, by then I will find some people to replace you and Leo. Although, there's always the chance that my aunt may return with me to Belfast as our father's health is improving now Doctor Fraser is treating him.'

'That must be a big relief to you,' said Susan.

'You can say that again.' Addie yawned and stretched. 'Anyway, I must telephone my hotel and let them know what I'm about. I can't afford a hotel for a month so I'll stay here with Aunt Adelaide. I need to go and collect my bag.'

'Leo could drive you there and bring you back,' suggested Susan.

'Now why didn't I think of that,' said Addie with a twinkle.

–

Within half an hour, the car drew up outside the Arcadia hotel. Addie suggested that Leo come inside and wait in the smoking room. She noticed there were two men of about forty years old in there, enjoying a smoke and a coffee, talking about the Grand National in a fortnight. One had an Irish accent and they were discussing their chances of winning the Irish Sweepstake. She left Leo asking them which horse they fancied for the big race.

As she went over to reception where Mick was standing talking to his grandmother, she overheard mention that one of the first races of the flat season down south had been cancelled due to heavy falls of snow which had also cut off some villages.

The old lady smiled at Addie. 'You've come for the rest of your luggage,' she said.

Addie nodded. 'I'll be staying at my aunt's house for the coming weeks. You'll be wanting my room soon, anyway.'

'Let's hope so,' said the proprietor. 'We'll lose a lot of money if the weather around here worsens and the racing is cancelled.'

'Well, so far we seem to be missing out on the snow,' said Addie, 'and although the wind's got up, the rain seems to be holding off, too. I see you've a couple of guests in the smoking room discussing the National.'

'They're not guests,' said Mick. 'They dropped by here on the chance of being taken on. They were hoping there might be work for them here, believing we'd be busy.'

'That's tough on them,' said Addie.

'They're not the only ones.' said Mick. 'There's been ructions at Gladstone Dock. The White Star Line's RMS *Majestic* was due to dock and there was a stampede for jobs and the foreman was mobbed. The police had to be called in.'

'I hope no one was hurt,' Addie said.

'A stampede?' said Mike's grandmother. 'Someone's bound to have been hurt.'

'Anyway, can I get you a coffee, Miss Milburn, before you go?' Mick asked.

'Make it two cups,' she said. 'My driver is waiting for me in the smoking room.'

She left them and went into the room where the three men were still talking. Leo made to stand up, but she told him to sit down as she had ordered coffee.

'Miss Milburn, these two men, Mr John Moor and Mr Timothy Walker, are looking for work. Mr Moor can drive, and Mr Walker was a gardener for the owner of a country house in Ireland,' said Leo. 'Because they served together during the Great War and have worked at the same place in Ireland for years since, they would be prepared to work for joint wages and board and lodgings with your aunt without delay.'

Before Addie could respond, one of the men, who had greying hair and a full beard said, 'I'm a Liverpudlian, Miss Milburn, and I'd really appreciate it if you could arrange an interview for us with your aunt. Tim has a sister who has been in service and she is an excellent cook. Leo here has mentioned that your aunt needs a replacement for his future wife. I've been in Ireland long enough and would like to come home.'

Addie thought there was something about the Liverpudlian that she found likeable, but she also noticed he had a terrible scar on his face. 'What happened to you?'

'I was injured during shelling in the trenches.' He told her and she didn't ask any more questions as it was common to see older men with these sorts of injuries, and many didn't like to talk of their experiences.

'Do you have family?'

He nodded. 'But none that are reliant on me,' he said awkwardly.

Addie said, 'You mean you have no wife?'

'No,' he said after the smallest hesitation.

'What about references?' she asked.

Before he could reply, Mick entered with a tray of coffee and biscuits. He must have overheard part of the conversation because he said, 'Grandma has seen their testimonials written by the captain of the ship they served on during the war. He believes both men could turn their hands to anything. She can let you have them if that will help?'

'What about their previous employment?' she asked.

'His lordship and his wife were both killed in a train accident,' said Tim in a strong Irish accent.

'I see,' said Addie, doubtful but not showing it, wanting to help the two men and the sister. She thought of asking about the sister's references but decided to take a chance on the men and the sister; they looked so honest and reliable. She could be making a mistake because there were so many desperate men and women in the country right now. Still, she would go by her gut feelings.

She suggested the two men call at her aunt's house in the morning at eleven o'clock and Leo gave them a piece of paper with the address on. They thanked her and along with Mick saw her to the car. The Liverpudlian man opened the door for her and closed it once she made herself comfortable.

'I can't believe what I've just done,' she said.

'Your aunt did tell you to find replacements for myself and Susan. Sometimes fate gives you a helping hand and I don't think you'll regret it, Miss Addie,' said Leo. 'They both seem decent men to me and apparently, Tim's from the same village in Ireland as Mick's father, who runs the Arcadia. Sadly, the father suffered wounds and has never completely recovered.'

'Sad, well, let's just hope that my aunt accepts them and their sister. New people just might take her mind off Milly being with her mother in Ireland.'

Chapter Twenty-two

Milly linked her arm through her mother's as they left customs in Dun Laoghaire. 'It seems ages since I've seen you,' she said.

'But at least you replied to my last letter,' said Bridget.

'I had to let you know the time of the ferry I was taking. I've kept the most interesting news until I arrived because I wanted to see your expression,' teased Milly.

Bridget nudged her in the ribs. 'So, you hinted at in your letter. Don't keep me in suspense then.'

'I left Barnaby's daughter at Grandmother's.'

'Her brother is still alive!' exclaimed Bridget.

'He's a widower with three children and lives in Belfast,' said Milly. 'He isn't in good health, though. Hopefully, he'll improve now he's being treated by Doctor Fraser.'

Bridget bit her lip. 'Your grandmother was convinced he was alive, so I wonder if she was right about your daddy and he's still alive and kicking as well?'

'It's a different situation, Mammy. Stop worrying. You've officially been granted a divorce for desertion. You're free to marry again.'

'True, and I won't have the family on my back this time saying my marriage isn't a proper one because I married a non-Catholic. Let's go into Dublin city centre and have something to eat and drink and then go shopping.'

Milly stood with her arms folded across her chest, gazing at her mother in an ivory figured gown with a crossover bodice and wide lapels with silk revers and long sleeves. The skirt was slightly flared and was mid-calf length. On her head, she wore a cream velour hat trimmed with coney rabbit fur.

'What do you think?' asked Bridget in a tremulous voice. 'I certainly didn't have a dress like this when I married your father. We were both nervous wrecks and I just wore my Sunday best.'

'You look wonderful,' said Milly. 'Aren't you glad that Andrew Fraser saved you from drowning all those years ago?'

'I can't believe what I did now,' retorted Bridget. 'I've sent him and Anne an invitation to the wedding.'

'Have you heard back from them?'

'Yes, they're coming. They'll bring the baby.'

'What about Kyle?'

'I mentioned inviting him to Andrew and Anne, but they told me to expect to be turned down as he and Jane are busy preparing for their own wedding.'

Her mother changed the subject. 'So, Barnaby and his children, will they be coming into money?'

Milly nodded. 'His mother left some money to be set aside for him and his children if he had any.'

'Does that affect you?' asked Bridget removing the hat and placing it in a box.

Milly shrugged. 'Grandma been spending money like there was no tomorrow. I doubt if there'll be any left for me by the time she goes.'

'Well, if you're ever short, love, just let me know. Sean's quite comfortable.'

'What's his surname, Mam? You never told me.'

'Lochraine,' said Bridget.

'How old is he, Mam?' Milly started on undoing the pearl buttons at the back of the dress.

'Forty-eight, but he's wearing well.'

'How's he taking you having a daughter of my age?'

'He likes the idea and can't wait to meet you.'

'What about Charlie?'

'He knows Charlie lives with his father, stepmother and grandmother, so he's not too fussed about it and he doesn't hold my past against me. He hopes though that you'll come and stay with us from time to time. You're getting older now Milly and soon you'll have your own life with your own fella.'

Milly thought of Jimmy when her mother said this. 'Does he have a nice house?'

'Of course, he's comfortably off, I told you.

As the shop assistant approached, Bridget said, 'It's your turn now, Milly. Have you any preference for colour?'

'Lemon, and I don't want any frills.'

'Did you hear that?' Bridget said to the shop assistant.

'I did,' she said, eyeing Milly up and down and taking a tape measure from around her neck. After taking Milly's measurements, she went away and then returned with a couple of dresses over her arm. One she held aloft from a hanger and was made of a heavy silk in a shade of amber.

Milly pointed at it and said, 'That's not lemon.'

'I know, miss, but I thought it would suit your colouring better and the style isn't so girlish. You're a young woman now. Shall I take the two over to a changing booth for you to try on?'

The upshot was that Milly went away with the amber dress and a Juliet cap in a coloured fabric that almost matched. Mother and daughter then went for a short walk alongside the River Liffy before going to Bridget's lodgings in a large Georgian terraced house not far from St Stephen's Green.

Later her mother cooked dinner for Sean. Milly was prepared to like her future stepfather for her mother's sake, but they had only begun eating the first course when she realised that she liked him for his own sake. He was not only polite and considerate of her mother, but she also received the impression that he was really listening to what Milly had to say, and that what she did say was worthy of his attention. Most importantly she did not get the feeling that he was putting on an act. When he talked about his laundry business, he made it sound interesting and an important service to the community and his very appearance spoke of how he acted on his own beliefs. Cleanliness was next to godliness in his opinion and made people feel better about themselves. He felt the same about exercise and listened to Milly when she advocated the Women's League of Health and Beauty which had been founded in 1930. Its members exercised often in the outdoors, making the most of the fresh air and performing synchronised movements.

'My friend Jane is a member and she wants me to join,' she added.

'But do we need to join a movement to keep healthy?' said Bridget.

'I suppose not,' said Sean. 'Perhaps it's a case of the more the merrier, and one can encourage others by meeting together.'

'I agree with both of you,' Milly said. 'I enjoy walking and cycling when I have the chance. Jane has a bicycle that Kyle gave her, so I've borrowed it the odd time since being back in Liverpool and cycled around the park.'

It wasn't until Milly and Bridget were alone later that it occurred to Milly that so far, no mention had been made of the O'Donnells.

'Who else on your side will be attending the wedding, Mammy?' she asked.

'Your great-grandfather, my mammy and our Kathleen and her daughter, Sheena.'

'I don't think I've met Sheena,' said Milly.

'No, she's married and lives in Belfast, her husband works in the shipbuilding industry. He had a well-paid job until the Depression happened. You remember Kathleen, though, don't you?'

'Yes, she's married to a farmer who lives a few miles away from Great-grandfather.'

'Her husband won't be coming as he can't leave the farm.'

'So, none of the great-uncles are coming either,' said Milly with a sigh of relief.

'They haven't been asked. Sean has no time for them.'

Milly said, 'I'm glad they won't be there to cause trouble.'

'Sean's thoughts exactly,' said Bridget. 'But someone who is coming, I've forgotten to mention, is a young man called Jimmy. Andrew mentioned that you were friends. I don't know why you haven't mentioned him, Milly?' said Bridget, cocking her head to one side with a smirk.

'I haven't seen him for a while and wasn't sure he'd want to come or even if he could afford the fare.'

'Well, he's going to come with Andrew and Anne. I'd like to meet this friend of yours.'

'He's still tied to his mammy's apron strings or her to him, in any case. Mam, don't go getting ideas into your head.'

Bridget smiled and shook her head. 'Young love,' she said softly.

'There you go,' said Milly, shaking a finger at her. 'I don't want you embarrassing me by saying such things when you see us together.'

'Cross my heart and hope to die I won't embarrass you, but if I think he's the wrong one for you I'll say so, though not there and then. Besides which, I'll have other thoughts on my mind.'

'You're not worrying that Daddy will suddenly turn up, are you?' Milly's colour changed from pink to white.

'I can't help worrying about that,' whispered Bridget. 'For once in my life I have the opportunity to be really happy and I can't bear the thought of things going wrong.' She anxiously twisted the skirt of her pinny between her hands.

Milly slipped an arm around her mother's shoulders. 'If he isn't dead, Mam, he wants us to believe he's dead, so he's not going to spoil that by turning up at your wedding. Besides, how can he possibly know you're getting married again?'

Bridget sighed deeply. 'That's true. But why should he want us to believe he's dead? He must know how hurt we and his mother would be.'

'Maybe he has enemies we know nothing about,' said Milly.

'Or he has another woman,' murmured Bridget.

'It's no use trying to guess,' Milly said. 'We must put him out of our minds and concentrate on enjoying ourselves on your wedding day and in the future.' She hugged her mother against her. 'I can't wait to see Jimmy's expression when he sees me in my bridesmaid dress.'

Bridget returned her hug and then looked at the clock on the mantelshelf. 'It's time we had some sleep. Are you sure you'll be all right on the sofa?'

Milly flashed her a look that spoke volumes.

'I know,' said Bridget, smiling wryly. 'You've slept in worse places.'

As Milly changed into her nightie and settled herself on the sofa with a pillow and a sheet and blanket, she said, 'When are Kathleen and Sheena and her husband coming to Dublin?'

'The day after next. I thought tomorrow after I've seen to wedding matters, we could visit Trinity College. I've always wanted to see the Book of Kells which is kept there, it's an ancient book in Latin. Sean says the illustrations are wonderful.'

'Suits me,' said Milly. 'Odd that I've never thought that you liked that kind of thing.'

'That's because ancient manuscripts never came up in our conversations,' said Bridget.

Milly had to admit that the Book of Kells was worth seeing as was Trinity College and it would be enjoyable behaving like a tourist with her mother. She was also excited about seeing Jimmy soon, as well as Anne and Andrew, and meeting Sheena who was a first cousin.

–

Afterwards, the O'Donnells all met up in a pub near College Green. As soon as she met Sheena, Milly liked her instantly. She was a fairy-like creature, petite and dainty with hair like spun gold, and eyes the colour of hazelnuts.

It took her a bit longer to decide whether she liked her husband, Pat, but that was most likely due to his being reserved and more of a man's man as Kathleen had hinted. He was broad-shouldered and muscular.

Fitting, she thought, for a welder in the shipbuilding industry.

He left his wife and mother-in-law to gossip with Bridget and Milly and her grandmother O'Donnell as soon as it was polite and went for a pint at the bar with Milly's great-grandfather instead.

Naturally, the main subject of conversation was the wedding and the baby that Sheena was expecting in October, much to Kathleen and the grandmother's delight. Even more surprisingly was the news that her great-grandfather had evicted the layabout Willie O'Donnell from his farm and updated his will leaving it solely to the only two men who had ever worked up a sweat helping him with the beasts and the crops.

'So, where has Great-uncle Willie gone?' asked Sheena.

'Most likely to the devil,' said Grandmother O'Donnell. 'He always finds work for idle hands.'

Milly was utterly surprised by her comment, but her grandmother had not finished.

'I overheard some of the women talking about our Willie and at first I couldn't believe what they were saying, that he had roaming hands and young girls couldn't be safe around him. I decided to confront one of them, believing she would back down and confess that she was a slandering bitch. However, she stood her ground and said I should speak to members of my own family. So, now's the time to speak if you have anything to say.'

Kathleen was about to speak, but Bridget interrupted her. 'Hang on a moment, Kath, I've something to say. Milly told me before she ran away that Willie had been interfering with her and I didn't believe her at first. It was only when she ran away that I thought things must have been really bad for her if she had to leave so suddenly.' Bridget looked at her daughter. 'I made some discreet enquiries in Cork, with the wives of those men who he played cards with and they said the same. He'd been barred from many family houses and had more than one black eye from brothers and fathers out to give him a thrashing for his actions.'

Then Kathleen spoke, saying that Willie had been over-familiar with her too when she was younger but did not go into intimate details. Their grandmother to said: 'Why didn't you tell me?'

'I didn't think you'd believe me,' whispered Kathleen.

Milly could not remain silent any longer. 'I could tell you about his obnoxious behaviour and that he was about to try it on again the day you all went to church. It was the day that caused me to run away to Liverpool because even Mammy wouldn't believe me. I couldn't take it any more,' she said breathlessly.

The four women stared at her and then Bridget burst into tears. 'My poor girl,' she sobbed. 'I'm sorry I didn't believe you right away. Can you ever forgive me?'

'Such disgrace should have been kept in the family,' said Grandmother O'Donnell.

'It was too late for that,' said Kathleen. 'He'd been too reckless and you know how talk spreads.'

'Well, now Willie has gone, things should quieten down,' said her mother. 'What he needs is to repent.'

'And to be taught a lesson he'll never forget,' said Bridget. 'If I come across him again, I'll wipe the floor with him.'

'I should get my Pat to take him out in a boat and drop him in the middle of the Atlantic,' said Sheena.

'Now there's a thought,' Kathleen said, smiling.

Chapter Twenty-three

Milly lay on the sofa that night unable to sleep, thinking over the earlier conversation and what Sheena had suggested Pat doing to her great-uncle Willie. No one had said anything about first having to find him. She knew from experience how difficult it was to find a person who didn't want to be found and would settle for Willie meeting an angry father or brother in a dark alley one night. Or perhaps an experienced woman who would teach him a lesson or two. Perhaps tying him to a bed infested with bed bugs and leaving him there for a couple of days.

Her grandmother O'Donnell would have them forgive him, but she knew that her mother and Kathleen never would, and neither would she. Milly knew a little of what grown-ups referred to as the birds and the bees, and only what her mother had told her after questioning her earlier that evening about what Willie had done to her. Bridget had seemed relieved by what Milly had told her and apparently, he hadn't gone as far as he might have.

'A good thing, sweetheart, when it comes to your getting married.'

Milly could have asked her mother what she meant, but part of her would rather not know. Even so Bridget continued in a vein that could have been utterly embarrassing to Milly if she had known more about the birds and bees, going on about her first time with her father, saying it had all been over very quickly and then he had gone asleep.

'I used to think it was a miracle that I managed to conceive you,' said Bridget with a tiny laugh. 'At least your father was a gentle soul, not like him who will be nameless.'

Milly had ended the conversation by saying, 'Can we go to bed now, Mam? I want to be bright and chirpy when Jimmy, Anne and Andrew arrive in the morning.'

Milly turned over and almost fell off the sofa but eventually she nodded off and did not wake until Bridget roused her and told her that it was seven o'clock in the morning; a pot of tea was made and she had toasted and buttered some soda bread. Milly would have to get a move on if she wanted to be there to welcome Jimmy, and the others at the railway station.

Milly wasted no time and scoffed her toast and gulped down her tea before donning her jacket and hat. She glanced at her reflection in the mirror and twiddled with the strands of hair that peeked out from beneath her hat and prayed that Jimmy would like what he saw.

Bridget said, 'Stop admiring yourself and let's go!' She tugged her daughter's arm and Milly allowed herself to be dragged to the front door.

'I do believe you're almost as excited as I am to see my friends.'

'I am, but it's not just that, I forgot to mention that Sean wants to take us all to lunch, so we need to be at the hotel where they're all staying for half past twelve.'

They made it to the station with minutes to spare and waited at the barrier while the passengers streamed along the platform. It was Bridget who spotted Andrew first and shouted his name and waved frantically, causing Milly to follow the direction in which her mother was looking, then Milly caught sight of Jimmy and her heart seemed to bounce in her chest and joy flooded her whole being. She tried to call his name, but emotion had her by the throat and his name was just a breath of sound. Then he was at the other side of the barrier and she could have sworn he was several inches taller. His eyes met hers and he smiled, and she knew that everything was all right between them.

'Hello, kiddo,' he said, once through the barrier taking her hand. 'You look wonderful, so grown-up in fact that I'm going to have to stop calling you kiddo.'

'You could call her Mildred like I do sometimes,' said Bridget, taking him in from head to toe.

Jimmy shifted his gaze to Bridget and offered his hand. 'How do you do? I presume I'm addressing the bride-to-be and you are Milly's mother?'

Milly said, 'Mammy, this is Jimmy, my very best mate.'

Bridget took Jimmy's hand and shook it warmly. 'I'm very well, thank you, and I'm so pleased you'll be at my wedding.'

'It's my pleasure,' he said.

She beamed at him and then turned to greet Andrew and Anne who were carrying their beautiful baby daughter, Christina, leaving Milly and Jimmy to move away and greet each other more privately.

'This is a right turn up for the books, isn't it?' he said.

'I know, I never foresaw it,' Milly replied. 'I do believe, though, that Sean's going to make her happy and I couldn't ask for more.'

'Not even to have your dad in his place?' asked Jimmy thoughtfully.

'I can only go by Mammy's words that she now has the chance to be happier than she has ever been.'

'Good for her,' said Jimmy. 'And what about you?'

'I'd be very happy if you greeted me with a kiss,' she said boldly. 'It's been so long since I've been this close to you.'

Jimmy did not need to be asked twice and they embraced. Milly surrendered herself to the wonder of the moment, even so she could have sworn she heard her mother say, 'Young love isn't it wonderful.'

It was Anne who said, 'Genuine love in any form and at any age is wonderful.'

Greetings over with, they all moved away from the barrier and towards the exit with Bridget informing them that they were going to meet Sean for lunch, so would need to get a move on.

'What about their luggage, Mammy?' Milly asked.

'We'll take a taxi to the hotel,' said Bridget. 'No need for you to worry.'

Milly refrained from saying, I'm not worrying I just want everything to go smoothly but they all managed to squeeze into the same taxi. Sean was already at the hotel and suggested they went straight into the dining room after arranging for his guests' luggage to be taken up to their rooms.

The atmosphere over lunch with the extended O'Donnell clan was cheerful if not completely relaxed as several of their number could not forget the search for Bridget's previous husband and that his whereabouts were still unknown. Yet his name was never mentioned and Milly was relieved when Sean made his excuses, saying he had to return to work as there were several matters he had to deal before his wedding. He did suggest that his guests linger over their coffee, adding that he would see them tomorrow in church as he wasn't bothering with a stag party because he wanted to have a clear head and feel his best for tomorrow.

Andrew was relieved that he wouldn't have to attend a men-only night out, which meant leaving Anne alone with Christina when they were both tired out, so, he and Anne went to reception and asked for the key to their room. Jimmy did the same, wanting to change into something more casual, planning afterwards to pick Milly up from her mother's lodgings.

–

When he came for her later that day, after having a cup of tea with Bridget and answering some questions about his background while Milly got ready, the two of them set off to explore Dublin.

'It's not as big as I thought it would be,' he said.

'Ireland isn't a big country so doesn't need a capital the size of London or even Liverpool,' Milly responded.

'I must admit I've come to regard Ireland like a younger brother to England,' he said, gazing down at the swirling water from one of the many bridges that crossed the Liffy. 'Though I can see it's not like that at all for the people who live here.'

'Would you say Liverpool is bigger?' she asked.

'Wouldn't you?' he countered.

She nodded. 'A lot of its citizens have Irish blood, though.'

'I know.' He grinned. 'We're a right mixture. Some of it is due to it being a port and situated where we are. I'm part Welsh, as well as English, Scots, Irish and Scandinavian.'

'So, you're really a thorough Briton with a touch of Viking,' she said, giggling.

'It wouldn't surprise me if most Brits have a touch of Viking,' he said. 'Even the native Irish probably do.'

'I think the Vikings did land in Dublin,' she mused. 'Them being great seafaring explorers.'

'They sailed along the Lancashire coast, landed in Formby, a few miles from Liverpool, so it's not surprising they crossed the Irish Sea,' said Jimmy. 'Do you think it's that touch of Viking that has helped make the natives of these British Isles such a seafaring race?'

She screwed her face up in thought. 'Not necessarily. It's more down to us having so much coastline. Anyway, the Celts reached Ireland earlier than the Vikings and they came from way across Europe, some settled in Western Spain and France.'

'What do you feel you are?' he asked. 'Where do you want to live for the rest of your life?'

'Where do you?' she asked, looking serious.

'I asked you first,' he said. 'I know your mam would like you to stay here in Dublin.'

Milly frowned. 'She told you that?'

'I wouldn't be saying so if she hadn't,' he replied with a shrug.

'Of course, stupid question.' She bit her lower lip, 'I tell you now, Milly. I couldn't settle over here.'

'Nobody was asking you to,' she said with the toss of her head.

'Your mam was sounding me out,' he said. 'If I was going to heed any mother, it would be me own.'

'And I wouldn't blame you,' said Milly. 'She has no one else but you and a sister who's hundreds of miles away.'

He stared at Milly with a slight smile tugging at the right corner of his nicely-shaped mouth. 'That's a problem, of course. If she lived closer to me aunt, she wouldn't be so interfering and possessive of me.'

She returned his stare and said slightly breathless, 'Why are we talking like this? You're making it sound so important where we should live in the future, sure there are loads of places I want to see yet!'

He took her hand and toyed with her fingers. 'Surely you know I care about you? I know we're only young, but I love you and I don't want there to be miles of sea between us. I want us to be together forever.'

Before she could say anything, he brought her against him and pressed an eager kiss against her lips. Her lips yielded to the pressure of his and when they eventually drew apart to take a breath, she said, 'Are we a courting couple then?'

'Don't ask daft questions,' he said. 'Of course, we are. Now give us another kiss, kiddo!'

She gave him another kiss or two and then, hand in hand, they returned across the bridge towards the city centre. 'You really should see the General Post Office building on O'Connell Street while you're here,' she said. 'It was almost destroyed during the Easter Uprising in 1916. Only the façade remained of a beautiful Georgian building after it was shelled because the rebels took their stand inside it. Two years ago, it was almost completely rebuilt, and Mammy says it looks as good as it ever did. Although, you can still see artillery scars on the walls.'

They went to see the building that had played such an important role in Irish history before going on to seek the cool greenery and restfulness of St Stephen's Green where they stayed talking, and he told her about what it was like

275

growing up without his own father. She told him about having met Addie and how she looked forward to meeting Addie's brother and sister and their father Barnaby.

'I do know about them,' said Jimmy. 'It's Doctor Fraser who's been attending Barnaby in Belfast lately. He seems to be on the mend.'

'Perhaps we could go up to Belfast before returning to Liverpool,' she said.

'We couldn't stay long,' said Jimmy. 'I have to return to work.'

'Of course,' Milly said. 'We could leave after the reception tomorrow.'

'Andrew and Anne and their baby would probably go to Belfast with us,' said Jimmy. 'They'll want to see Doctor Fraser.'

They spent a little longer huddled up together on the park bench before he escorted her back to her mother's apartment and after spending an hour there, Jimmy returned to the hotel where he discussed his plans with Andrew and Anne.

–

Milly served breakfast to her mother in bed the following morning, the day of the wedding, and by the time Bridget and Milly had returned from the hairdresser's and were having a coffee and blackcurrant jam butties, her great-grandfather and Kathleen were knocking on the door.

'You're early,' said Milly, opening the door.

'Granddaddy was fretting about being late,' Kathleen said, easing her way past Milly.

Milly stared at her great-grandfather who was wearing a pinstriped suit, white shirt and what appeared to be a shot-silk, jade-coloured tie. 'You look so smart and handsome,' she said, taking his arm and pulling him into the apartment. She kissed his weather-beaten cheek. 'You really should dress up more often and you'd have all the rich widows after you.'

'I don't need a rich widow,' he rasped. 'I have enough money to get by and womenfolk to keep house for me – but thank ye for yer kind words, girlie. Now where's our Bridget – a bagful of nerves, no doubt.'

'She has them well under control if she is,' said Milly. 'Now would you be wanting a cup of tea and a bite to eat after the journey?'

'Tea would be just the thing, girlie, and I wouldn't say no to a slice of crusty bread slathered in some best Irish butter.' She led him to a chair and lowered him into it before going into the kitchen.

Kathleen joined her a few minutes later. 'I never thought this day would come,' she said. 'Granddaddy has accepted our Bridget remarrying, otherwise, he wouldn't be here and giving her away.'

'Has he said anything about my daddy?'

'Not a word! He's fond of you but never had any time for Joseph. They were so different, and in a way, he was glad that your parents weren't married in our church because that way he could believe it was a non-marriage.'

Milly felt as if she had been punched in the belly. 'But what does that make me in his eyes?'

'His great-granddaughter.' Kathleen raised her eyebrows. 'Let that suffice.'

Milly knew the wisest course to take was to drop the issue. After all her future lay in Liverpool. She nodded and made a pot of tea and buttered a slice of the cottage loaf she had bought earlier and returned to the living room where her mother and great-grandfather were talking.

Two hours later Milly and Bridget were dressed in all their finery and being oohed and aahed over by Kathleen and Sheena. As she was the only bridesmaid, Milly travelled in the automobile that was taking the bride and her great-grandfather to the church. The driver had allowed plenty of time for the journey; what with it being St Patrick's Day, the capital was busy. The ceremony was to take place in Sean's parish church which had a pleasant atmosphere and did not smell overpoweringly of incense. The priest had a voice that was heavily accented and much of it was in Latin, so that Milly could not understand a large part of what he said, and so she just let the words pass over her head.

It was a relief when the service was over with no interruptions, there had been a point when Milly was worried that her father would enter the church and call the service to a halt, but thankfully that didn't happen.

After the priest, she was the first person to congratulate her mother and her new stepfather. Only when they left the church, Milly could have sworn she saw a familiar face in the crowd outside and a cold shiver trickled down her spine. Yet later at the reception in the hotel where Andrew, Anne and Christina and Jimmy had spent the previous night, her mood was relaxed. The wedding feast was delicious and after the speeches, there was dancing to a local group of musicians which set most people's feet tapping; she and Jimmy spent most of the dances in each other's arms.

Chapter Twenty-four

Early the following morning Milly was ready and waiting outside the apartment block for the taxi that would take her to the railway station where she was to meet Jimmy, Andrew, Anne and Christina to catch the train to Belfast. When suddenly a young man wearing a loud check suit and a beige trilby sidled up to her and grabbed her arm roughly.

'I thought I'd find you here,' he said, glancing up at the apartment block.

She gazed with horror into Liam O'Donnell's face and would have screamed if he had not covered her mouth with his hand.

'The police are all after me in Liverpool because you told them it was me that was after Barnaby Milburn's money.' She managed to bite one of his fingers and his hand slithered down to her chin and seized it and he banged her head against a wall. 'That should shut you up for good,' he snarled and called her a rude name, but to her relief just at that moment she heard a vehicle draw up and she tore herself away from Liam. Despite her aching head, she managed to pull further away from him and threw herself at the taxi driver who was stepping out of his cab.

The taxi driver caught her and said, 'What's going on here?'

'Mind yer own bloody business,' snarled Liam.

'That's lovely language that is, in front of this young lady,' said the taxi driver.

'She's no lady,' snapped Liam. 'She's me sister and she's eloping with an Englishman.'

'He's a liar,' gasped Milly, attempting to focus on the face of the taxi driver. 'He's a villain and a criminal and they are after him in England, he's the kind yer read about in the Sunday papers scamming innocent folk. I'm Miss Milly Martin, are you the taxi for me?'

'I am,' he said, opening the door of the rear passenger seat. 'You just step inside, miss.'

Liam would have prevented her from doing so, but she managed to hoist up her Gladstone bag and ram it into him. He staggered back and she took the opportunity to accept the taxi driver's helping hand and climbed into the taxi as Liam collapsed onto the pavement. She told the taxi driver to get cracking as she had a train to catch and he drove off just as Liam struggled to his feet, waving a clenched fist after the taxi.

Milly slumped against the back of the seat, her head aching. She uttered a thank you to the driver. 'I don't know what I'd have done if you hadn't come along when you did,' she said.

'Just call me your knight in shining armour,' he said with a chuckle.

'What is my knight's name?' she asked, resting her head against the back seat.

'Joseph,' he replied.

'My daddy's name is also Joseph,' said Milly, feeling as if she was drifting. 'It's a grand name. Sadly, he's dead.'

'It's a saint's name,' said the driver. 'Could be your daddy is with the saints and keeping his eye on you.'

'I'll hold that thought in my mind,' she said, sinking against the back of the seat again and closing her eyes.

'So, which station are we going to, miss?' he asked.

'Amiens Street Station. I'm meeting friends there and we're going to Belfast to see family,' she said faintly. 'Then in a few days we'll take the ferry home to Liverpool.'

'It's a grand place is Liverpool. I have relatives there who live in the Dingle. Are you knowing the Dingle?'

'Yes, it's to the south,' she said, her eyes felt heavy and she attempted to force her eyelids wide apart, but they kept closing again.

When they arrived at the railway station, the taxi driver called her name, but she had difficulty getting up and opening the door, so he stepped out and opened it for her. She almost fell out, though somehow he managed to prevent her from landing on the ground.

A few moments later Jimmy approached the taxi. 'Milly, are you all right, love?'

The driver looked at him. 'Are you one of the friends she's meeting?'

'Yeah,' said Jimmy, taking hold of Milly. 'We're going to Belfast to meet her great-uncle and his children.'

Joseph released her reluctantly. 'Are you sure the pair of you aren't eloping?'

'Why in the Lord's name should you think that?' asked Jimmy, hoisting Milly upright.

Her eyelids fluttered open. 'Jimmy!' she said. 'We haven't missed the train, have we?'

'No, kiddo! But we'd better get a move on. Andrew and Anne are waiting on the platform for us.'

Her brow puckered in thought as she glanced at the taxi driver. 'Hello, Joseph. Have I paid you?'

'No, Miss Martin.'

She fumbled in her coat pocket and produced a handful of change and passed the lot over to him. 'I hope that's enough for my knight in shining armour.'

Jimmy glanced at the money and took a ten-shilling note from his wallet and handed it to Joe. 'Whatever you've done for her, thanks mate.' Then he dragged Milly away, half carrying her. 'So, what happened?' he asked.

She blinked at him. 'The Big Bad Wolf tried to carry me off.'

'You mean an O'Donnell?'

She nodded. 'Can I explain once we're on the train? I don't feel so good.'

Jimmy said no more but hurried as best as he could to the barrier where he could see Andrew, Anne and Christina waiting on the other side. As Jimmy approached with Milly, he could see that they looked worried.

'What's wrong with her?' asked Anne as soon as the younger couple were through the barrier.

'An encounter with an O'Donnell from what I gather,' said Jimmy grimly, as they hurried as best they could along the platform until they came to an open door of the Belfast train. They managed to find an empty carriage and Jimmy literally fell into a seat with Milly, almost squashing her.

None of them spoke for a while and then Anne handed Christina to Andrew and crossed the carriage to help disentangle the couple. She sat on the other side of Milly, and said gently, 'Tell us what happened, Milly?'

'He banged my head against a wall,' she said, her eyelids lifting. 'It was Liam. I was scared, but I managed to bite him and hit him with my bag.'

'So, you ran away?' Andrew asked.

Milly shook her head and winced. 'Joseph came and helped me into his taxi,' she slurred the words. 'I'm safe now. The Big Bad Wolf can't get me.' She snuggled into the crook of Jimmy's arm and would have closed her eyes, only Anne said, 'You have to stay awake Milly, until we can get you to a doctor.'

'With a bit of luck, Grandfather will be at home and up and about. He'll know what's best to do,' said Andrew.

The train journey took over two hours and the others kept Milly awake by asking questions and talking about all sorts of things like their favourite singers and films, but eventually they arrived in Belfast and took a taxi to Doctor Fraser's home. Once he was told the story and had given Milly a quick examination, he had his car brought round and went to the hospital with her, telling Jimmy there was no point in him accompanying them.

At the hospital, Milly's head was x-rayed and the wound cleansed and dressed. She was told she had a concussion and she was allowed to leave under Doctor Fraser's care. A bedroom was prepared for her by the doctor's housekeeper and she was tucked up in bed and told to rest. Throughout the day she had the company of Anne or Jimmy to keep an eye on her.

It was to be two days before the doctor allowed visits from various members of the family she had never met before. Milly was adamant that no one was to tell her mother what had happened for fear of her calling off her honeymoon. As for Jimmy and Andrew they took their leave of her before then as they had to return to work. Jimmy kissed her gently on the forehead before he left. 'If I ever get hold of that Liam O'Donnell, I'll give him the thrashing of his life.'

'You'll do no such thing,' she told him. 'I don't want my future husband going to prison on account of that n'er do well.'

Chapter Twenty-five

Milly was more than surprised when, a few days later, she awoke to see her grandmother Martin had entered the bedroom, and was standing at the foot of the bed. For several moments Adelaide stood there, silently gazing down at her granddaughter, then she said, 'This is a fine kettle of fish. I hope you still think it was worth attending your mother's wedding?'

'Don't start, Grandma,' said Milly. 'It was a lovely wedding and Mam and Sean are very happy.' She paused. 'Anyway, I'm glad you made the decision to come to Belfast and hope you believe it was worth making the effort.'

'It was a terrible crossing,' said Adelaide, feeling her way around the bed and sitting on it sideways before reaching out for one of Milly's hands. 'Although, my eyesight isn't what it was, so I couldn't see Barnaby's face clearly at first and age has altered the timbre of his voice. When he hugged me, and said the things he had to say, it was so much like the old Barnaby I thought my old heart would burst with happiness.' Her voice quavered on the last few words and a tear ran down her cheek.

'Oh, Grandma, I'm so happy for you,' said Milly through the lump in her throat. 'Where is he? I'd like to see him.'

'You'll see him shortly. He's just having a few words with Doctor Fraser. We owe him so much. He brought Barnaby back from the edge and now he's helped you when you were in need.' She dabbed at her eyes with a lace-trimmed handkerchief.

'What about your niece and nephew?'

'They're here with Addie. She has a young man here in Belfast who she knows will be eager to see her, so she'll be staying in Belfast. He's her old boss at the mill and he's asked her to marry him. She's going to put the share of the money my mother left her into the mill after they are wed.'

'That's wonderful,' said Milly. 'I have a young man too, Grandma, but it will be a few years before we can wed.'

'I'm glad to hear it,' Adelaide said. 'Marry in haste, repent at leisure.' She paused. 'Now tell me how you feel now you've had time to rest after that monster of an O'Donnell attacked you?'

'Safe,' said Milly. 'It's lovely having so many people caring about me.'

'Why shouldn't they care about you? You're my grand-daughter and a nice, caring person, despite the mistakes your parents made.'

Milly hid a smile. 'Thanks for the compliment, Grandma. Does this mean I'm back getting a mention in your will?'

'Impudent girl,' said Adelaide, looking embarrassed. 'I never took you out of it. I only wish your father was here.'

'Well, he isn't, so we'll just have to make the best of things.'

'Yes, but I'd have sworn I was right about him still being alive.' Adelaide sighed.

Milly said, 'How are Susan and Leo?'

Adelaide frowned. 'You haven't heard that they're married now and going up to live near her mother? They're going to be working at the children's place up there.'

'You must feel bereft,' said Milly.

'I was shocked to the core, but I've two men and one has a sister who've taken their place. They're going to do all that's necessary in the house and gardens to make my life comfortable. The men's names are Timothy and John.'

'What about a companion?'

'Barnaby and his two younger children are returning to Liverpool with me and will be staying at the house in Waterloo for a while.' She paused and squeezed Milly's hand. 'Of course, you are welcome to come and stay any time you like.'

'Thank you, Grandma, I'll definitely come and visit with Jimmy once we're back in Liverpool. Kyle and Jane are getting married on the Whit weekend.'

'You mean they're marrying in May?' said Adelaide. 'That's unlucky.'

'No, in June,' Milly said.

'But Whit's in May this year. It's a moveable feast,' said Adelaide. 'I'm sure the vicar will put them right.'

–

When she woke there was no sign of her grandmother. Then she heard a knock on the door and a male voice asked if he could come in.

She called, 'Yes, you can come in!'

The door opened and an elderly man in a rust-coloured suit entered the bedroom accompanied by two young persons. Milly held her arms out and said, 'Come over and say hello!'

Father and children rushed over. 'I'm Luke,' said the boy.

'Hello, Luke,' said Milly. 'I'm delighted to meet you.'

'I'm Eileen,' said the girl, her face pale and drawn as she held out a hand to Milly.

Milly shook Eileen's hand, thinking she and Eileen were both of an age when they could be good friends. She thought that Barnaby must have really been getting on when he fathered his son.

'How do you do? I'm so pleased to hear that you're coming to Liverpool. It'll give us a chance to get to know each other.'

'I'm looking forward to it as well,' said Eileen. 'Auntie Adelaide has said we can go shopping in Liverpool for new clothes. Will you come too?'

Milly nodded. 'I need a new outfit for the wedding of a couple of my friends.'

'I don't want to go shopping for clothes,' said Luke.

'We'll go to the football match and to Aintree to see the horseracing,' said Barnaby, resting his hands on his son's scrawny shoulders.

'They both need feeding up, Barnaby,' Adelaide said from the doorway.

'That's because there's been a slump on, our Adelaide,' he retorted. 'The girls did their best working their socks off to put food on the table, but it wasn't easy for them what with me ill in bed.' He hesitated. 'But now those days are behind us and life can only get better.' He smiled down at Milly. 'It's good to meet you, girl, and thank you for all your efforts to find me. You have mine and your grandmother's eyes.'

Another knock on the door and Anne popped her head in. 'Grandfather said you can get up for breakfast if you want, Milly.'

'Of course, I do want! But we'll need to get this room emptied first,' said Milly. 'And I'll need to unpack some clothes.'

'I'll run a bath for you and then help you dress,' said Anne, shooing out Barnaby and his two children.

No sooner had they gone than Milly threw back the bedcovers and slid her legs over the side of the bed. 'Well, that went off well,' she said. 'And surprise, surprise, I'm back in Grandma's good books again.'

'She's been given something else to live for,' said Anne as she bustled out of the room.

Milly thought how true that was because surely, the return of her twin, and the arrival of two nieces and a nephew, had to help her recover from the loss of her son.

It was bliss lying in the musk and lemon-scented bathwater and to have Anne gently shampoo her hair. Afterwards she helped Milly into a lemon-coloured blouse and the green-flecked tweed suit she had bought in Edinburgh last year, not forgetting a green felt hat with a yellow ribbon around the brim.

'You do look nice,' said Anne. 'Now let's go downstairs and have some breakfast.'

'I'm desperate for a cup of tea,' Milly said, thinking she also wanted to get back to Liverpool to be reunited with Jimmy.

Within a short time, Milly and Anne were seated at the table in the dining room overlooking the rear garden, eating poached eggs on toast and occasionally glancing out of the window at the birds feeding at the bird table.

Barnaby, Eileen and Luke had returned home, and they were all to meet later, including Milly's grandmother Adelaide who had gone to her hotel. They were going to have a picnic where they would discuss plans to return to Liverpool.

-

'We can't waste time, we need to buy our tickets today,' said Barnaby, having gulped down the last bite of a ham sandwich as they all sat on picnic blankets in Belfast's Victoria Park. 'What with it being the Grand National in less than a week's time, the ferries are going to be busy.'

'Surely, they'll put extra sailings into operation?' said Anne, reaching for a beaker of lemonade and bouncing Christina on her knee.

'Aye,' said Barnaby. 'But you want to leave and join your man as soon as possible?'

'Of course,' she replied. 'And Christina misses her daddy too. I would have gone with him, but I wanted to see my Scottish cousin and her husband who are staying in Liverpool for the racing.'

'Then let's get the tickets today,' said Milly. 'Great-uncle Barnaby, you'll know where we have to go, so lead the way as soon as we've finished our picnic.'

He nodded and as soon as they'd all finished and called Luke over from kicking a ball, Barnaby, Anne and Adelaide headed for the ticket office while Milly, Eileen and Luke went to a picture palace to see a Sherlock Holmes film called *The Sleeping Cardinal* with Arthur Wontner playing the great detective.

Later at Doctor Fraser's house, Milly was told they would be taking a ferry to Birkenhead for Liverpool in the morning, so she would have to be up by five o'clock in time for the taxi to take them to the terminal.

Despite the early hour, there were plenty of people taking the ferry to Birkenhead, where Cammell Laird's shipbuilding yard was situated; a short trip on the Mersey ferry from Liverpool. Milly felt excited that she had these new members of the family to share the journey with; the last time she had taken the ferry to Merseyside she had been alone, and things had been so very different.

Chapter Twenty-six

Milly was extremely relieved when the boat eventually arrived at Birkenhead. Her grandmother was exhausted and so Milly suggested that instead of taking the ferry across the Mersey, they should go instead by taxi to Hamilton Square and take the underground train to St James Station, where all of them, bar Anne and Christina, could walk to the nearby Exchange Station and catch the Southport train to Waterloo. Anne planned on staying at the Arcadia Hotel in Mount Pleasant so she could see her cousin, Fiona.

Despite having been informed of the new staff that her grandmother had hired with Addie's assistance, Milly still expected to be greeted by Susan. Instead, the door was opened by an unfamiliar woman with a shock of carrot-coloured hair and a maternal figure. Her eyes were hazel, and her face was warm and welcoming.

'You must be Miss Milly, the mistress's granddaughter,' she said with an Irish accent. 'I'm Josie! My brother is Tim, the gardener and his friend, John, is the driver. Both are generally good about the place, turning their hand to anything.' She paused for breath.

Before she could say anything else, Milly held up a hand to stem another flood of words. 'It's lovey to meet you, Josie, but can you help us inside? My grandmother is worn out with travelling and needs her bed and a cup of tea.'

'The mistress's bed is made up, miss,' said Josie, stepping aside. 'And I've prepared a bedroom for her brother and nephew to share, as well as one for yourself and her niece to share.'

'Thank you, Josie. Now if you could fetch your brother or his friend, John, or both to deal with the luggage that will be great.' Josie wasted no time and was gone in a whisk of a squirrel's tail.

Adelaide led the way into the drawing room, leaning on Barnaby's arm and the rest of the family trailed after her. Following a sweeping glance around the room, he led her to a sofa and they both sat down. Luke curled up next to the cat on the rug in front of the fire, while Eileen and Milly sat on the other sofa.

'This is a lovely room, Adelaide,' said Barnaby.

She nodded in agreement. 'I hope that woman won't be long with the tea,' she murmured. 'I'm parched and I hope she thinks to serve some biscuits.'

Five minutes later Josie entered the room carrying a tray with the teapot and tea things, as well as a plate of fairy cakes and some sandwiches. She placed the tray on an occasional table in front of the sofa and asked, 'Did madam want to pour, or should I?'

'Milly, you pour,' said Adelaide. 'You know just how I like my tea.'

Milly did as she was asked, and at the same she was aware of men's voices in the hall. She waited until all cups were filled and her grandmother had two cakes and two triangular sandwiches on a plate next to her cup and saucer before leaving the room and speaking to the two men. Both paused in the act of choosing two pieces of luggage apiece as she cleared her throat, and they turned their heads to stare at her.

'Good evening, John and Timothy,' she said. 'I am Mrs Martin's granddaughter, Milly. I presume you with the red hair are Josie's brother, while you…' she paused, staring at the other man, '…are John?' She felt unnerved by the intensity of his stare.

He flicked the side of his forehead as if saluting her. 'I am, Miss Milly, and right glad I am to be here working for your grandmother.'

Milly couldn't miss the large scar on the left-hand side of his face that distorted his features and she thought he might still be attractive if he shaved off his beard, but he did have nice kind eyes, that seemed to bore into her own.

'I had best call Josie to show you which bedrooms to take the luggage.'

'And to whom each piece of luggage belongs,' he said. 'I think the Gladstone bag is yours, Miss Milly.'

She nodded, thinking he seemed to have an accent that was Liverpool mixed with a bit of Irish. 'Good guess,' she said.

'It has a luggage label with your name on.'

'Indeed,' she said.

Before Milly had time to call Josie, she appeared. 'You were wanting me, Miss Milly?' she said.

'Yes, Josie. I want you to go with John to make sure he puts the right luggage in the right bedrooms.' Milly proceeded to show the maid which luggage belonged to whom before returning to the drawing room, wondering if one day John and Josie were making a match of it.

Yet in the days that followed, Milly noticed only an ordinary affection between the two when she saw them together. Besides which they were kept busy with their own duties most of the time. It was Barnaby who suggested to his sister Adelaide that John should take Milly to Jimmy's mother's home the next day, dropping off Adelaide and Eileen in Liverpool centre, so they could do some shopping and maybe have lunch there and see a matinee at the Empire Theatre or visit the Paramount Picture Palace.

'You seem to be very knowledgeable about Liverpool's places of entertainment, Barnaby. The Paramount wasn't there when you ran away as a boy,' his sister said.

'They do get a mention in certain newspapers even in Ireland,' he said, 'especially when it's known that large numbers of Irish will be visiting the city during the week of racing at Aintree, and many Liverpudlians buy tickets for the Irish Sweepstake.'

'Of course,' she said. 'How could I have forgotten it was National week coming up? I wonder if the King and Queen will be attending, or the Prince of Wales?'

'I've not noticed it mentioned, but it does say that the crowds were out in Chester to give the Duke and Duchess of York a right royal welcome in the sunshine.'

'They'll probably be staying at the Duke of Westminster's place,' Adelaide said. 'The Duchess of York is lovely and has marvellous dress sense. I'd love to see her in the flesh, not just the newspapers or magazines.'

'From what I've read about her she's fond of horses, too,' said Milly, who had been listening to the exchange. 'If she has a horse running at Aintree it could be the duke and duchess who'll be watching the big race on Friday.' She put down her copy of *Woman's Weekly* and said that she was going up to change and so what time should she ask John to bring the car round?

Her grandmother glanced at Eileen and said, 'Could you be ready in half an hour?'

'I'm ready now,' she said. 'I just need to fetch my coat and hat.'

'Good,' said her aunt. 'It could take me twenty minutes to decide what coat and hat to wear.'

'I'll say half an hour then,' said Milly and left the room.

She found John polishing the car and told him to bring the car to the front in half an hour. 'May I ask where we're going, Miss Milly?'

'My grandmother and Eileen wish to go shopping in Liverpool city centre, so they will be dropped off there and then you'll take me on to Kensington to my young man's home. He lives there with his mother. His father was killed in the war.' She wondered why she felt compelled to add the information about Jimmy's parents. After all John was a servant and had no need to know about the latter. Although from her experience servants always seem to find out about such things.

'Right, you are then,' said John.

There was something in those words that triggered something in her memory but for the moment it eluded her, so she left him and went indoors and up to her bedroom where she changed into the brown skirt flecked with yellow and green, a cream crêpe de Chine blouse and a brown-flecked jacket with a fur collar. Her rust-red cloche hat was of wool with a flower at the side made of the same material. Her stockings were of silk and her strapped shoes were of brown patent leather. She put on brown kid gloves and picked up her handbag before hurrying downstairs.

'My, you do look smart,' said Barnaby. 'Your Jimmy is a lucky young man.'

'Thank you, Great-uncle Barnaby,' she said, brushing his cheek with her lips.

'Come on,' said Adelaide. 'The day will be half over before we get there if you don't get a move on.' She ushered the girls out to the waiting car.

John had the front passenger door open for her and he helped her into the seat. The two girls climbed into the back and John closed the doors before getting into the driving seat. He revved the engine as Barnaby hurried to open the gate to allow the car through and he waved them off.

Milly was relieved when after it was decided what time and where John should pick up his mistress and her niece, they dropped off her grandmother and Eileen outside the Bon Marché on Church Street, because Eileen had gone on and on about Milly not going shopping with them. It had taken all her patience not to lose her temper, especially when her grandmother suggested Milly seeing her young man was not important right now. Eventually, Milly had turned her back on Eileen and stared out at the passing shops along Stanley Road and began to sing 'It's a Long Way to Tipperary'.

She pulled a face and decided not to dwell on what had gone on earlier or it would spoil the rest of the day as she leaned back in the centre of the back seat. 'You know which way to go to Kensington, John?'

'Yes, Miss Milly,' he said, turning and heading for Lime Street, past the Royal Infirmary towards Kensington and Prescott. She was looking at the back of John's head in the driver's seat as they made their way, and she still felt unnerved in some manner, but couldn't put her finger on why.

She gave him directions once they passed Kensington Library and soon he was coasting slowly along the street where Jimmy lived, careful to avoid the children playing rounders, giving them fair warning of his approach by sounding his horn. A couple of women were gossiping while resting their hands on the end of the pole of their brooms. They turned their heads at the sound of the car hooter, watching as it drew up at the kerb closest to the house Milly indicated.

With the engine still running, John stepped out of the car and opened the rear door and helped Milly out. 'What time would you like me to be here to collect you, Miss Milly?' he asked as the front door of the house had opened, and Jimmy walked towards the car. His mother stayed standing in the doorway.

'You don't have to collect me, John,' she said. 'I'll make my own way home.'

'I'll see you home,' said Jimmy. 'Although, I must say that's a super car. I bet she goes like a dream. My boss wants me to take over the driving of the work's van, so he's teaching me to drive. He learnt when he was in the army, so we have some hairy moments as he's not finding it easy what with all the traffic on the roads in Liverpool; he's only just bought the van and hasn't driven for years.'

'You'll soon pick it up,' said John.

'Maybe you could give him some lessons in the car,' suggested Milly. 'I'll ask Grandma's permission when I see her.'

Both John and Jimmy looked dubious but did not say anything. Meanwhile, Jimmy's mother, Cathy, remained silent, her arms folded across her chest, watching them. Milly glanced at her and gave a tiny wave but the only response she received was a hunched shoulder as the older woman turned and went inside.

Milly said, 'I think we'd better join your mother, Jimmy. I suspect she's getting impatient, wondering what we're talking about.'

Jimmy nodded, and taking her hand, said, 'Let's go then.'

Both bid a ta-ra to John, who said, 'Right you are then,' before driving away.

Cathy was in the act of putting the kettle on the fire as they entered the kitchen. 'So, who was that man?' she asked, turning to face them. Her eyes went to their interlocked hands.

'John is my grandmother's driver,' answered Milly.

'Jimmy said she was comfortable. No doubt she has a big house.'

'Big enough to put up family when they visit,' Milly said. 'But it's no mansion.'

'I can't understand why you want to have anything to do with our Jimmy. He can't give you what you're accustomed to,' said Cathy, roughly.

'Mam!' exclaimed Jimmy. 'You've said far too much. Another word along such lines and I'm out of here for good.'

'You can't mean that,' said his mother aghast.

'I can,' said Jimmy, 'and I do. Say you're sorry to Milly right now, or we both go and don't come back.'

'It's all her fault,' said Cathy. 'She's turned your head. Me and this house aren't good enough for you now.'

'That's enough, Mam!' shouted Jimmy. 'I love Milly.'

'And I love Jimmy,' Milly said in a shaky voice. 'Surely, you and I can get on and be friends for his sake?'

'You're too young to know what love is,' sneered Cathy, 'and I don't need you for a friend.'

Milly lost control of her emotions. 'Neither do I need you, but I was prepared to put up with you because I could guess how you must feel.'

Cathy danced with rage and her face screwed up until she looked completely unlike herself. 'You can have no idea how I feel. You're a spoilt rich kid! You've no idea what it's like to lose someone you love to war, to be left with a child to rear and with no money!'

'That's where you're wrong,' said Milly, switching her attention to Jimmy. 'Didn't you tell your mam about my daddy?'

He shook his head. 'I tried but she wasn't interested. I did think Anne might have told my aunt and she'd have told Mam, them being sisters.'

'Our kid was too wrapped up in Anne's baby to take much notice of me,' said Cathy. 'At least I had something she has never had, a child of my own.'

'She's always been good to us both, though,' said Jimmy. 'Why are you so bitter?'

'Go on, stick up for her! It was easy for her to throw money about. She had a man bringing in a wage. I suppose this one here will have all your earnings now,' she spat out.

Milly said, 'I'm going. I've had enough.' She did not look at Jimmy but left the kitchen without another word.

Chapter Twenty-seven

Jimmy managed to catch up with Milly before she reached the tram stop. He stood beside her and reaching down, grasped her hand. 'I'm sorry about Mam. Surely you understand she's scared of losing me and being left to manage all on her own?'

She wrenched her hand out of his grasp. 'Of course, I understand, but her behaviour took me back to when Mammy and Grandmother were forever arguing and that last quarrel when Mammy took me out of her house, screaming that Grandma would never see me again – although she called her something worse than Grandma. My life was hell. I was barely ten years old and my daddy was missing and they both wanted me to love them best.' She stared at him. 'You do understand what I'm getting at?'

Jimmy hesitated and then nodded, saying, 'What am I to do?'

'If we ever marry, you have to accept that your mam and I will never live under the same roof. She has to let you go if she wants to be a proper grandmother to any children we might have.'

'You want me to choose between the pair of you!' he exclaimed, choking on the words.

'No, you have to put me first if I'm to be your wife one day.'

'The Bible says we have to honour our parents,' Jimmy said.

'It also says that a man must leave his parents and cleave to his wife and they become one flesh,' countered Milly.

Jimmy smiled wryly. 'You have all the answers, don't you?'

'I wish,' she said. 'But I'm not asking you to cut her out of our lives, only that she accepts that she must not be so possessive where you're concerned.'

He screwed up his face. 'It won't be easy.'

'No, it won't. You'll have to work at making your mother see that she only has one choice if the three of us and any children we might have are to be a happy family.'

He opened his mouth and she prayed he was going to agree with her, but he only said, 'Here's the tram.' He helped her aboard and they went downstairs where she sat on a seat next to the window and he sat next to her. Neither of them spoke until the tram arrived at the Rotunda Theatre where they crossed Scotland Road and caught one that would take them to Waterloo.

Jimmy said in a low voice, 'You're very sure we will marry.'

'It's what I want, and I thought it was what you wanted despite us being so young.'

'It is, even though I knew there would be trouble ahead.'

'There's always troubles in life, but where there's a will – a way through can be found,' she said. 'I know through experience.'

'Your dad's fate is still unknown, though,' Jimmy said.

Milly sighed. 'One doesn't always get what one wants, but at least Great-uncle Barnaby is back, along with

Eileen, Luke and Addie, although Addie is staying in Belfast to marry her boss.'

No more was said, and when they left the tram instead of going straight to her grandmother's house, they went for a walk on the beach. The tide was on its way in and there were plenty of people about, enjoying the sea breezes and watching the ships heading for the estuary and the Irish Sea.

An hour later the two left the beach and feeling hungry, Milly suggested they have something to eat at her grandmother's house. They had almost reached the gate when her grandmother's car passed through the gateway and stopped.

'Want me to take you and Jimmy up to the door, Miss Milly?' John asked her, sticking his head out of the driver's window.

'No thank you, John, we're grand,' she answered.

John smiled and nodded at her, saying, 'Right you are, Miss Milly.'

She stared at him intently and it was like a lightbulb going off in her head when suddenly she realised exactly who John really was. 'It is you, Daddy, isn't it?' He had always used that phrase when he was at home and now everything fell into place.

'I wondered if you'd ever recognise me. You were so young when last we saw each other,' he said.

'What happened?' she said, her face lighting up as her spirits soared. 'Why didn't you come and find me?'

'I had my reasons, lovey.' His voice was low and gentle.

'Can't you tell me?' she asked, aware that her grand-mother was staring at her driver in disbelief.

'I'd find it difficult,' he said with a sigh.

At that moment Josie and Tim appeared from around the side of the house. They stopped in their tracks, watching the tableau being played out before them. Then both moved forward and took up position either side of Joseph. 'Everything all right?' asked Tim.

'Tim, my daughter has recognised me at last. Not by my looks but my words,' said Joseph.

Milly noticed a look that passed between the two men that was more like the look that passed between a man and a woman. Immediately, she remembered her grandmother showing her the photograph of her father with his friend, Tim. Also, of the conversation with Old Jack at the sailor's home and his comment about the two men never being seen without the other. Suddenly it all became very clear to her.

'Right you are, Daddy,' said Milly, going into his arms at last. 'I'm so glad to see you again. I think I do understand. It was all to do with love.'

Joseph exchanged glances with Tim. 'I knew from the moment I began to read stories to you, when in no time at all you were telling them back to me, that you were a clever girl,' he said huskily, kissing the top of her head. 'Although, love isn't the whole story.'

They were separated by Adelaide. 'Joseph, is it really you?' she asked, wishing aloud she could see his features clearly through the fog of her failing eyesight.

'It is, Mamma,' he said, enclosing here in his embrace along with Milly. 'I'm sorry I worried and hurt you both.'

'What about Mammy?' asked Milly.

'I heard she's remarried,' said Joseph. 'I'm glad. I could never have made her happy in the years to come and would have been desperately unhappy trying to do so. The only good thing to come out of our marriage is you, dear daughter.'

Barnaby arrived just in time to hear those last words. 'What's going on?' he asked.

'You're going to have difficulty believing this, Barnaby,' said Adelaide. 'But John is my son Joseph.' Her voice broke.

'I don't get it,' said Barnaby, gazing at John, Tim and Josie. 'Why pretend to be someone you're not?'

'Because I didn't know who I was,' said Joseph, fixing his uncle with a stare before shifting his gaze to Tim. 'Will you explain what happened after the ambush?'

Tim nodded. 'Although, perhaps it would be best if we went indoors and all sat down, it's going to take some time.'

There was a murmur of agreement and Barnaby led the way, holding his sister by the arm. They went into the drawing room and made themselves comfortable. Tim and Joseph taking up a stance by the fireplace while the rest sat down in a semi-circle, bar Josie, who vanished into the kitchen to make a pot of tea.

Tim asked the ladies was it all right with them if he smoked? They nodded and he and Joseph lit cigarettes and offered the packet of Players to Barnaby and Jimmy who both refused.

'Joe and I have known each other for years as most of you know, having met while serving in the merchant navy during the war,' said Tim. 'We hit it off straightaway and survived many a scrape together.'

Joseph interrupted him. 'Tim saved my life during those years and later. The last time being after the ambush in Ireland.'

'Who's telling this story?' Tim nudged Joseph in the ribs before continuing, 'It was a case of being in the wrong place at the wrong time. The ambush was meant for Michael Collins who had signed the treaty in London and some of his supporters and it happened near a crossroads in the countryside in County Cork where we had stopped to check which road we should take for the coast. Next thing we knew all hell broke out and we had to run for cover. Neither of us had any intention of getting mixed up in the civil war in Ireland.'

'The O'Donnells thought I was pro-treaty,' Joseph interjected. 'But I thought it was none of my business getting involved as an Englishman, and the Irish people should make up their own minds.'

'Joseph had been making some enquiries about Barnaby in the area, and now I believe the attackers thought we were somebody else. There was a sudden explosion out of nowhere and while I was thrown some yards away behind some bushes, Joe was buried by the soil and material that was flung up. I didn't realise straightaway what had happened to him. My head felt fuzzy and I ached all over and was scratched about the face and hands. At first, I couldn't make sense of anything, then I heard voices, and from what was being said I realised they were the attackers, then came the noise of vehicles starting up. I began to remember where I was and what had happened. As soon as I felt it was safe, I disentangled myself and set about seeing if I could find out what had happened to Joe.' He paused to take a cup of tea from his sister's hand and swallowed a mouthful of it before going on with his tale. 'It was obvious from the layout of the ground that there had been some burials and I knew I just had to dig and see who was there. That was when I discovered that Joe was in no grave but loosely covered by the debris from the explosion. Fortunately, he was still conscious but had a nasty injury to his face which was torn apart. He was gasping for breath and thrashing about and he was in a bad way – trembling all over and babbling like a baby. What was even worse was that he didn't recognise me, nor could he remember who he was.'

'But you were able to tell him,' said Adelaide.

'Aye, but it didn't mean a thing to him,' Tim responded. 'He couldn't connect it to family or home. I decided to take him to my sister's husband's farm and help him recover his memory.'

'Why didn't you get in touch with his wife's family in Ireland?' asked Adelaide.

'I wanted to, but he had no memory of them and besides he had told me in the past he had no love for them and didn't trust them.' Tim turned to Barnaby. 'You were in Ireland during that time, you must remember what it was like?'

Barnaby nodded.

'You could have written to me,' said Adelaide sniffily.

'I could scarcely read or write, and I wasn't going to take risks,' said Tim, a flush in his cheeks. 'And besides Joe could not remember the address, and when we did try, you had moved to a new house.'

'So, most of the time Daddy's been missing, the pair of you have been living on your brother-in-law's farm?' said Milly.

'Aye,' said Tim. 'Then gradually bits of Joe's memory returned, and we decided to find work on the mainland, so took the ferry to Holyhead and did seasonal farm labouring in north Wales as we had little money, working our way towards Liverpool, until we crossed the border into Cheshire where we found more work and we met Leo. It was an answer to all my prayers when he told us he was working for Joe's mother. The rest you know,' Tim said, smiling.

Milly remained silent trying to absorb all the detail.

'So, what are your plans now, Joe?' asked Barnaby. 'Are you going to continue living here and take care of your mother and daughter?'

Joseph glanced at Tim and then his daughter and mother. 'I'd find it difficult to settle in one place. Tim and I are going back to sea.' Before Adelaide and Milly could protest, he added, 'Not immediately. I want to spend some time getting to know you both all over again.'

'Then perhaps Eileen, Luke and I will continue to live here with you, Adelaide,' said Barnaby.

'And I'll go and stay with Jane until she and Kyle get married,' said Milly. 'She'll want someone to look after the house while she and Kyle are in Llandudno on honeymoon, although they might decide to move into his house.'

'Who are Kyle and Jane?' asked Joseph.

'Good friends of mine,' Milly said. 'You'll be meeting them, as well as my other friends Anne and Andrew who live in Southend-on-Sea in Essex.' She paused. 'What about Mammy? When Jimmy and I eventually get married, she's going to find out you're still alive, Daddy.'

Joseph scratched his head. 'Truthfully, lovey, I don't know what to do about your mother now she's remarried.'

'There's no rush,' said Jimmy. 'It'll be a few years before I can afford a home of our own and besides Milly will need your permission to marry, Mr Martin, now you've turned up.'

'And your mother won't give her permission, so we'll have to wait until you're twenty-one,' said Milly.

'What has your mother got against my daughter, Jimmy?' asked Joseph.

Jimmy groaned. 'It's complicated.'

'She's a widow and she doesn't want to let him go,' Milly said sadly. 'And I know it's not a good idea for a mother-in-law and daughter-in-law to live under the same roof.'

Joseph stared at her but remained silent.

–

The following morning Joseph drove Milly to Jane's house near Newsham Park. He surveyed the front of the house in surprise. 'I thought your friend would be living in one of the big houses overlooking the park,' he said.

'Jane used to live in Ormskirk with her mother in a cottage which was left to Jane. After her mother died, she wanted to move to Liverpool to be near relatives and now she rents it out. Andrew is her brother.'

'But didn't you say he lived in Essex?' said Joseph.

She nodded. 'But he grew up in Liverpool as did Anne. He's a newspaper reporter and his grandfather's a doctor in Belfast.' She paused and climbed out of the car and went and banged the door knocker.

The door opened in no time to reveal Jane standing there fully dressed and wearing a floral apron. 'Milly! I wondered when you'd turn up.' She glanced at the car and the man who had just climbed out. 'Who's this?' she asked.

'Jane, let me introduce you to my father, Joseph Martin.' She paused as Jane gasped and swayed, reaching out for the door jamb. 'Daddy, this is my dear friend Jane Fraser.'

Joseph hastened to grip Jane's arm as he thought she appeared about to swoon. 'This must be a shock to you,' he said. 'I'm guessing you know all about me from Milly.'

'Yes!' She said. 'Am I to presume you turned up at Bridget's wedding?'

'No, I wouldn't have done that,' he said.

'Let's go inside,' suggested Milly. 'I'll make a pot of tea and you can hear Daddy's story.'

'Yes, do come in,' Jane said, releasing herself from Joseph's grasp and leading the way inside. She indicated that he be seated on the sofa and she sat in one of the fireside chairs. 'I wish Kyle was here to hear your story,' she said. 'We're engaged and our wedding is the beginning of June, the weekend after Whit weekend.' Milly was relieved that Jane knew she'd had the date wrong for Whit.

'I'll go and make a pot of tea. I think we need it.'

Jane stared at Milly. 'I'll need to go shopping for my gown and your bridesmaid dress soon, Milly.'

–

'You must be fond of her,' he said, glancing at Jane as his daughter entered the room, carrying a tray.

'She's good company, never a dull moment when she's around. Although she's taken off a few times in her attempt to discover what happened to you. Your mother being convinced you were still alive.'

Milly grinned at her father as she placed the tray on the table and began to pour tea into three cups. 'She was the same with Barnaby as you must have heard, Daddy?'

Joseph nodded, accepted a cup and saucer from her and took a sip of tea. 'Perfect,' he said.

'Now your story, Mr Martin?' said Jane.

'Call me Joe,' he said, before launching into his story.

Having already heard it, Milly excused herself, saying she was going to the telephone box to call Anne and Andrew to let them know the news.

It took some time to get through to Anne but eventually she was speaking to her and the news was received with the delight she had expected. She was running out of coins by the time the conversation ended with the sound of a baby crying at Anne's end.

'I'll have to go, love,' she said. 'But no doubt you'll be hearing from Andrew soon.'

On the way back to Jane's house, Milly saw Franny who must have been on her way to Cathy's house. The girl looked at Milly with dislike and said, 'So, you're back! How was your mother's wedding?'

'It went off like a dream,' replied Milly. 'You still seeing Liam?'

'Is there any reason why I shouldn't be?'

Milly shrugged. 'I just wondered.' She thought to herself whether Franny knew anything about the fraud or the attack, or that Liam needed to keep his head down.

'Anyway, Liam's heard all about you from a visitor from Ireland.'

'And who would that be?' Milly felt uneasy hearing this.

'Your great-uncle Willie. He's come for the races with Liam.'

'Thanks for telling me, and if you've any brains you should keep away from him yourself. Ta-ra,' Milly walked on to Jane's, convinced now that it was Willie who was caught up with the business with the fraud. Her blood ran cold, could she now expect him to turn up around here?

Chapter Twenty-eight

Milly told Jane and Joseph about her conversations with Anne and Franny.

'Time, I think to talk with her mother,' said Jane. 'She needs to be aware that Willie is not to be trusted. The sooner Kyle arrives the better I'll like it. He'll know what we should do about Willie if he starts making a nuisance of himself.'

'You could both stay at Mother's house in Waterloo,' Joseph said.

'I can't,' said Jane. 'This is my home and I'll be damned if I'll let him scare me away.'

Milly stared at her in surprise, thinking it was the first time she had heard Jane swear.

A short while after, Kyle arrived, and the first comment he made after being told about Willie and being introduced to Joseph, was that Jane should have a word with the local bobby on the beat. 'It wouldn't surprise me if the police are already on the lookout for any Irishmen looking for trouble – arson, bombs in pillar boxes are favourite nuisance acts of the militant republicans. Those things aside you could just ask him to keep an eye on your property.' He paused. 'It could be that a watch is already being kept on Liam's family.'

'Will do,' said Jane. 'We can also tell them that Liam might be at the races. Have you time for a cup of tea?'

Kyle glanced at the clock on the mantelshelf. 'All right, I'd like to hear some more of Milly's father's story.' He sat down.

Jane and Milly went into the back kitchen, leaving the men to talk.

'Kyle took everything in his stride,' said Milly.

'Yes, there's not much that gets him in a tizzy.'

'Yeah, he's a good bloke,' Milly said, drying a saucer.

'So, what next?' asked Jane, making another pot of tea.

'The Grand National and then Easter weekend,' said Milly. 'Then the big event – your wedding the first weekend in June!'

'Yes, I got myself in a real muddle over Whit, but the vicar put me right,' said Jane with a wry smile. 'Are you going to the Grand National?' she asked, changing the subject.

'The family are going,' said Milly. 'I've never actually been before, but Grandma and Great-uncle Barnaby used to go with their parents and some other relative. Grandma is a great royalist and was hoping to see the Duke and Duchess of York there. They are staying with the Duke of Westminster while they pay a royal visit to Chester. The difficulty now for Grandma is that her eyesight is worsening, and she can't see very well.'

'I see,' said Jane. 'Are you doing anything special for Easter?'

'Going to church, and after lunch we're going to Southport.'

'On Easter Saturday, I'm having a visit from Violet,' said Jane.

'Violet!' exclaimed Milly. 'So, she's back in Liverpool.'

'Back with her husband and children. Apparently, she and her cousin fell out.'

'Did she mention me?' asked Milly.

'Of course, she wants to know if you want to continue with your lessons.'

Milly said, 'Yes, tell her I do.'

'Will do,' said Jane. 'I wish you could be here.'

'I need to spend time with the family.' Milly placed cups and saucers on a tray.

'So, what do you think about my daddy?'

'I'm wondering how your mother would feel if she was to see him alive and well.'

'You're thinking she might be wishing she hadn't married Sean?' Milly bit down on her lower lip.

At that moment Joseph called out that he would have to go as he was meeting Tim in town to do some shopping and go down to the Pierhead. They both called ta-ra and carried on with their conversation.

'What do you think? You've met Sean.'

'I think she's best not seeing Daddy. What would it achieve? Tears all round.'

'You don't know that.'

'No, I don't.'

'What if your mother and Sean went on to have a baby?'

'Are you thinking that with Daddy still alive, the marriage could be declared null and void and in that case the baby would be illegitimate?' Milly almost dropped a cup.

'No, of course not! She's divorced now, but she needs to know he's alive, its important so that they can all move on with their lives. Even though he isn't dead, she's learnt to live without him, and you say Sean is a lovely fella.'

'Maybe you're right,' Milly said.

'What about Charlie's father?' Jane asked.

'They weren't married thankfully,' Milly groaned. 'Oh, why did my parents have to make my life so complicated!'

'War!' said Kyle. 'It messed up lots of people's lives.'

She nodded. 'I'll do what you say. I'll speak to Daddy first and either he or I will write to Mam. In the meantime, what about Liam and Willie? They could dodge the bobby on the beat. They're crafty.'

'Surely you could stay at your grandmother's and Jane could stay with Auntie May,' said Kyle.

'I've not leaving this house,' said Jane fiercely. 'They might break in and mess it up.'

'You're going to have to leave it when we get married,' said Kyle.

She stared at him and her chin wobbled. 'We haven't made a decision about that yet,' she said tremulously. 'I'm staying here. I'm not going to be scared out of my home.'

'Don't be so stubborn,' said Kyle with an unusual flash of anger.

'I'll ring Andrew and see what he advises,' said Jane.

'So, you'll listen to him rather than me,' said Kyle.

'He's my brother,' Jane said. 'We can both talk to him and Anne. They have plenty of sense.'

'And I don't, is that what you're saying?'

Milly put her hands to her ears and cried, 'Will you both stop it? You sound like Mammy and Grandma when they'd argue over what was right for me. I'll speak to Great-uncle Barnaby and Andrew and Anne. I don't want you two falling out.'

'Does that mean the three of us crowd into the telephone box?' said Kyle, tongue in cheek.

'No,' replied Milly. 'I'll go first and then I'll come out and you two can go in together.' She was wanting them to go with her just in case Willie and Liam should turn up and confront her.

Shortly after they strolled down to the phone box, Milly looking over her shoulder in case Liam or Willie were following behind. Luckily there wasn't a queue and Milly spoke to Andrew first, telling him all about Liam still being on the loose, and now with Willie in tow it would seem.

'They're a dastardly duo,' he said, with feeling, but he decided to discuss it with Anne first before giving her any advice.

Eventually Anne came on the telephone and said, 'Do you remember the policeman who was such a help after Andrew rescued your mother from the Mersey?'

'Of course,' said Milly. 'Kyle has met him, too, at the orphanage. Do you think it would be a good idea to get in touch with him?'

'Yes,' said Anne. 'He knows you and some of your story and so could talk to the inspector in charge of your local police station and push to make sure your, and Jane's, story is taken seriously.'

She thanked them both, adding that she was looking forward to seeing them at Kyle and Jane's wedding. She replaced the receiver and left the telephone box saying, 'No need for you two to speak to them as I'm sure you'll agree with what they've suggested.' She told them what had been said.

'Now, why didn't I think of that?' said Kyle.

'I didn't think of it either,' Milly said.

'And I wasn't on the scene when Andrew rescued your mother,' said Jane.

'Well, now that's settled,' said Kyle, picking up that evening's newspaper which had just been delivered and looking at what it had to say about the racing at Aintree that day. 'Thinking about what you said about your grandmother, Milly. There's a whole section here about the ladies who attended and what they wore.'

He passed the page over to Milly who glanced through it and read out aloud about '...Lady Ursula Filmer-Sankey and her short coat of summer ermine over a beige tweed frock, and Lady Royden's long coat of glossy-brown pony skin... There's loads more,' Milly said, 'but I don't want to bore you. I'll just mention... Mrs Noel Cornelius who wore a black velvet coat with a huge collar of snowy lapin and a little hat in black and white...' She paused. 'Oh, and in the county stand there are loads of sirs and even a lord and an earl, as well as a Mrs Brunel-Cohen wearing a smart green suit of tweed with a tie of leopard skin.' She handed the page of the newspaper back to Kyle.

'Isn't a lapin a hare?' said Jane.

Kyle nodded. 'Poor thing. I wonder if it was trapped in Canada or in the mountains of Scotland.' He fell silent, glancing at the listings for the cinemas that evening. 'How about a trip to the flickers tonight?'

Both Jane and Milly were in favour, so they visited Irwin's grocery shop and purchased some sausages, potatoes, onions and a packet of Bisto, while Kyle went to the Seamen's Orphanage the other side of Newsham Park to ask the matron for the name of the policeman who had been of such help to Anne and Milly several years ago.

'That'll be Sergeant Blakeman,' said Matron. 'A really good man. You should be able to get in touch with him at the police station in Tuebrook.'

–

As soon as Kyle mentioned the name Sergeant Blakeman to Milly, she remembered the sergeant who had been party to enabling Anne to take Milly on occasional outings from the orphanage while her mother was in hospital. Kyle decided to visit the police station the next day. That evening they went to see Gracie Fields in *Sally in Our Alley*. She was a singer and comedienne and had been a well-known performer both in music hall and on gramophone records before she became a star of the silver screen.

The three of them enjoyed the film despite its sad moments and were in a good mood when they returned to Jane's home, only to discover that the front door was ajar. Kyle signalled that he would go inside while Jane and Milly waited outside.

Jane exchanged looks with Milly and followed him inside. As for Milly, she decided to go to Marjorie's house a few doors away and tell her and Gordon what was happening.

She was about to bang their knocker when she was seized from behind and dragged away from the front door. She managed to free a muffled scream and aimed a back kick at her assailant before a hand was clamped more firmly over her mouth.

Sharp teeth bit her ear painfully and a male voice snarled, 'Another sound from you and you'll be sorry, bitch.'

Liam, she thought! She raked the back of the hand that covered her mouth with her fingernails. He withdrew it sharply, swearing vociferously and she dug her elbow into his midriff before pulling away from him and yelling for Gordon and Robbie at the top of her voice, before turning and facing Liam who was doubled up.

The door behind Milly opened, and she fell backwards and was prevented from hitting the floor by Gordon who jerked her upright. 'What's going on?' he asked, setting her aside and glaring at Liam. 'When are you going to learn, lad? I warned you to stay away from here.'

'It's a free country, old man,' said Liam sullenly. 'Why don't you go back inside and mind your own business?'

'You, cheeky young sod,' Gordon said, and before Liam could move out of the way, Gordon threw a lucky punch which caught Liam on the jaw and jerked his head back.

Franny appeared as if from nowhere and prevented him from hitting the ground. 'I'll have the police on you, Mr Anderson. Why don't you pick on someone your own size?'

Milly snorted. 'You need to buy some specs, girl. Liam's a good six inches taller than Mr Anderson,' she said. 'But you go and call the police and Liam will get banged up faster that you can say Jack Robinson. Don't you know he's wanted for fraud and a serious assault on me before this?'

'You're a lying cow,' screeched Franny. 'What reason has he to attack you?'

'He's after my grandmother's inheritance,' said Milly. 'But he's easily led and a bully. Even so he made a big mistake by doing so. By the way, Franny, if I'm not mistaken here comes a policeman.'

It wasn't just any policeman, it was Sergeant Blakeman who having received Kyle's message, had decided to come along to visit Jane and Milly, as well as hoping to see Kyle there, but in his grasp, was Willie. 'I found this fellow lurking around then fleeing the scene and recognised him from your description,' he said.

It still turned Milly's stomach to see her great-uncle Willie but he now cut a pathetic figure as he wriggled in the sergeant's tight grip.

-

In no time at all, two more policemen arrived in a Black Mariah and despite Liam and Franny's protests and Willie's excuses, they were taken off to the clink. Franny received a strong warning and was encouraged to stop fraternising with criminals. Several of the neighbours had come outside to see what was happening, and were cheering the policemen on.

With Willie and Liam dealt with, Milly decided to stay the night with Jane and return to her grandmother's first thing in the morning. Kyle chose to stay as well, saying he didn't trust Liam not to enlist the male members of his family to attempt to get revenge on Milly and her friends. Kyle stayed downstairs keeping watch, while Sergeant Blakeman had several bobbies keep an eye out for any trouble.

He told them the following day that Liam and Willie had admitted cooking up a scheme to pose as an imposter to get the Milburn inheritance. 'Their plot was full of holes,' the policeman said. 'Not least, them using the picture of one of Willie's card-playing cronies as a substitute for a real one of Barnaby Milburn. They'll have got caught eventually whatever happened, but you were lucky not to have a more serious injury, Milly. They'll both be looking at a stretch for this.'

Chapter Twenty-nine

Grand National Day dawned and Milly was glad of Kyle's offer of a lift to Waterloo in his van before he headed off to work. Kyle also asked Milly to ask her father to get him a ticket for the Irish Sweepstake when he was buying his own and handed her the money.

Milly entered her grandmother's house and immediately Adelaide pounced on her. 'Why didn't you come home last night, instead of staying at Jane's? You knew we were going to the races today.'

Milly removed Adelaide's hand from her arm, thinking she did not like mentioning that her grandma's failing eyesight would mean she wouldn't be able to see any of the races or any royalty if they were there. 'We went to the flickers and when we returned the house had been broken into and then there was a tremendous commotion because I was attacked. Fortunately, the police turned up and Great-uncle Willie and Liam were arrested,' she said excitedly.

'Goodness, you have had a time of it,' said Barnaby who had arrived in the middle of her tale. 'But now's the time for you to make up for lost time if we're to get a good spec for the horses and the betting on the race.'

Milly dug into her coat pocket and took out a couple of coins. 'Kyle asked me to ask Daddy to get him a ticket for the Irish Sweepstake when he buys one for himself.'

Barnaby sighed and pocketed the money, deciding to do that himself as his nephew was finishing some job in the garden with Tim and he was best not being disturbed if he was to drive them to Aintree in time for the early races.

Milly hurried upstairs and found Eileen brushing her hair in front of the dressing table mirror. 'You're back at last,' she said.

'Obviously, if I'm here,' said Milly. 'That's a lovely dress and jacket you're wearing.'

'Aunt Adelaide bought it for me.'

Eileen stood up and did a twirl. 'What are you going to wear?'

'The bridesmaid dress that Mam bought me,' replied Milly, reaching into the wardrobe, wondering if she had time for a quick bath. She hung the dress on its hanger from the picture rail and rushed out of the room, praying the bathroom would be empty.

Her prayer was answered, and she wasted no time running a few inches of steaming water and lavender bath crystals in the tub and adding some cold water, not wanting to scald her posterior. She lowered herself into the water with an appreciative sigh and washed herself all over, leaving her hair dry. Reluctantly she stepped out of the bath, dried herself and returned to the bedroom wrapped in a towel to put on clean underwear and stockings and the dress of amber silk. She brushed her hair and donned the matching amber cap before applying some Pond's Vanishing Cream and a touch of lipstick. She stepped into her shoes, picked up her brown gloves and handbag before hurrying downstairs.

'My, you do look nice,' said her grandmother.

'Lovely is the word, Mamma,' said Joseph, putting an arm around his daughter and hugging her.

The weather was perfect, and they were soon on their way. Once in the car, Barnaby said, 'I want to get a spot near one of the jumps.' Joseph agreed with him. Adelaide voted to watch from the finishing line and Eileen echoed her choice, but Milly said she would go with her daddy, so the group split up on arrival as the site was swarming with people.

Milly noticed there were lots of women dressed in their finery among the crowds, all placing bets at the Tote. Seeing the horses jump was thrilling, although Milly did not realise how upsetting it would be seeing the horses fall. Several horses fell and their jockeys lost their seats, but fortunately neither horses nor jockeys were fatally injured. To her delight, Grakle won at odds of 100 to 6. Barnaby grinned as he told her that was the horse he had backed. Later it was discovered that Kyle had the same horse in the Irish Sweepstake. Joseph and Tim had also backed Grakle, while Adelaide and Eileen had backed a shilling each way on a horse that came in third, so they had some winnings, but not a lot.

It was as they were leaving the racecourse, that to her great surprise, Milly caught sight of her mother and step-father. She was at a loss what to do and was in a right tizzy, she realised. Should she slip away and say hello to them, she wondered, when unable to look away her mother caught her gaze. Bridget's gaze shifted slightly, and her eyes widened. Milly guessed that her mother had caught sight of Joseph and recognised him instantly, despite his scar. Milly knew there was no getting away from speaking to her mother now and swiftly excused herself, merging with the crowd in the direction she had last caught sight of Bridget and Sean.

A few minutes later she came upon them and realised that her mother was wearing what looked like an expensive fur jacket. Milly suggested the three of them went and had some tea and cakes at a nearby café where she would explain everything. Sean was grim-faced and Bridget was all-of-a-tremble. Milly linked an arm through her mother's. 'There's no need for you to work yourself into a state, Mam. Daddy knows you've remarried, and he wants you to be happy.'

'That's big of him,' said Sean sarcastically.

Milly just looked at him wordlessly and was glad they had reached the café. They went inside the busy café, and she led them to a vacant table out of sight of the window, pulling out a chair for her mother to sit down on, before ordering a plate of cakes and a pot of tea for three at the counter. She was asked to sit down, and a waitress would bring it shortly.

Milly returned to the table and sank into a chair, relieved to rest her feet and her back. Bridget appeared to be miles away, while Sean was fiddling with his fingers.

'So, what happened to him and where's he been all this time?' he asked roughly.

'It was just bad luck that he and his mate were caught up in the fighting. During an ambush on Michael Collins, a grenade exploded, and Daddy and his mate Tim were caught in the blast. To cut a long story short, Daddy was a dithering, frightened and confused wreck, he had no idea where he was, who he was or who Tim was. It was obvious to Tim that the horror of being buried and the injury to his face and possibly being hit on the head had caused the damage.'

'Why didn't he take him to the O'Donnell farm?' asked Sean.

'He didn't trust the O'Donnells, so he took him to his brother-in-law's farm and Tim and his sister cared for him.' She changed the subject and began to talk about the Grand National and the crowds that had attended, asking whether her mother had seen anyone famous.

'I thought I'd caught sight of Winston Churchill, and of course Lord Derby was there and Lord and Lady Stanley as well as Lord Sefton. I did hear that the Duke and Duchess of Westminster had a barge on the canal with a party to watch the race,' said Bridget.

'I wonder what the duchess wore?' mused Milly.

But Sean was not letting the former conversation go. 'Why couldn't your father have let his wife and mother know the truth years ago?'

'Apparently it took years for him to remember he had a wife, child and mother,' said Milly tersely. 'When he eventually did so, he recalled that he had sent his wife and daughter to his mother in England, so guessed they believed him dead by that stage, but were safe and getting on with their lives without him.'

'So, how did he turn up in Liverpool, knowing Bridget had remarried?'

'Some friends and I had been searching for him for the last year or so and news gets around, as you must know,' said Milly. 'My grandmother's driver was marrying her housekeeper, and said he would find replacements for her, but as it was, by a twist of fate, Daddy's Irish cousin came across Daddy, Tim and one of his other sisters and they ended up working for Grandma without anyone realising. That was until the penny dropped for me.'

'So, your father and his mate are working for your grandmother,' said Bridget.

'Not permanently, they served on the same ship during the war and are talking about going back to sea. As for my grandmother she'll be having her brother Barnaby and his children to live with her.'

Bridget smiled. 'Fancy him turning up, as well. So, where are you living, and do you know who she's leaving her money and the house to now?'

'I doubt she has much money to leave as she's been spending like crazy. I divide my time between Grandma's and Jane's for now.' Milly resisted telling her about Willie and Liam's latest escapade, word would reach her soon enough. She reached for a butterfly cake as her mother poured the tea. 'I expect she might leave her money to Luke and Eileen. I just care about spending some time with Dad before he goes back to sea.'

'So, all's well that ends well,' said Bridget. 'Do you think your father will marry Tim's sister?'

Milly paused, cake halfway to her mouth. 'Somehow, I don't think so. He and Tim are such pals and their hearts are set on going places together.'

'Why doesn't that surprise me,' said Bridget, darkly. 'What about you and Jimmy? His mother is proving to be an obstacle to us courting, but that's not going to prevent us from seeing each other and we're prepared to wait until Jimmy's twenty-one before we get married.'

'As long as she doesn't offer the pair of you a home with her,' said Bridget. 'With her being so possessive of her son, it won't only be difficult for you but for him, too. You know from experience what it was like with your grandmother Martin and me.'

Milly nodded. 'Yeah, I was piggy in the middle and you two were always pulling each other to bits.'

'Too right,' said Bridget. 'I suppose one can't help feeling sorry for Jimmy's mother – what with losing her husband in the war, but she's not alone in that.'

'And she does have a sister as well as Jimmy. I just wish she'd go and move near her, but she's lived in that house since she married and it's full of memories of her husband.'

'Then you and Jimmy need to move away,' said Bridget. 'Why not come over to Ireland?'

'I like Liverpool,' said Milly. 'Besides Jimmy won't want to move too far away from his mother. They've been through a lot together since his father was killed, just like you and me went through a lot together when we left Grandmother Martin's house.'

Bridget's eyes gleamed. 'You could move across to the other side.'

'The other side of what?' asked Milly.

'The Mersey.'

'You mean to the Wirral?'

Bridget nodded. 'New Brighton. There are big houses over there made over into apartments, so I've heard.'

'Now there's a thought,' murmured Milly. 'If we could find an apartment over there for Jimmy's mother that would be great. She likes the seaside and an apartment would be easier for her to look after than a house. She'd feel more on a level with her sister in Southend-on-Sea. I'll speak to Jimmy about it and if he likes the idea, he can talk her round and once she's moved in, we can get married.'

'You could move into the house she has now,' suggested Bridget.

'No thanks,' said Milly. 'She'd be forever calling it her house. It's time I had a place I could call my own or mine and Jimmy's.'

Milly and her mother embraced, and though it was the ending of one story and the beginning of another for them both; Milly couldn't help but think it would take her mother a little more time to come to terms with it all.

–

When Milly arrived back in Waterloo, her grandmother pounced on her. 'What happened to you? One moment you were there and then you vanished.'

'I'm sorry if you were worried, but I'm a big girl now and able to find my own way about,' said Milly. 'The truth of the matter is I spotted Mammy in the crowds with my stepfather, and as she had seen me, I went over and told them about Daddy. It's important for her to know the truth so that she isn't forever looking over her shoulder and wondering about him.'

Chapter Thirty

Jimmy persuaded his mother to visit New Brighton with him and his aunt over the Easter weekend at the beginning of April after being in touch with his aunt Sal in Southend and telling her of his and Milly's idea. Immediately she consulted her husband and he had approved of her paying a visit to Liverpool to spend time with her sister and nephew.

The sisters reminisced about trips on the ferry to New Brighton when they were children and Milly heard Sal ask Cathy did she remember nagging their father about moving to New Brighton when they were children. She had wanted to play on the sands and look for crabs in the rock pools by Fort Perch Rock which had been built in 1820 to defend the coast from attacks after the wars with France.

'I'm a bit old for digging in the sand now,' said Jimmy's mother as they left the ferry.

'But you could have grandchildren after Jimmy and Milly are married,' said her sister, 'and don't frown at me like that, little sister. At least you're in a position to have grandchildren, you were lucky to have a child, unlike me.'

Milly glanced at Jimmy and smiled self-consciously as his mother said, 'I've never thought about having grand-children.'

'Think of it now,' said her sister. 'If you found yourself an apartment over here you could have your grandchildren to stay and take them crabbing and sandcastle-making. I envy you.' She sighed.

'But I don't live over here,' she said. 'Besides how could I leave the house which is full of memories of my fella?'

'You carry his memory in your heart and soul,' said her sister. 'And you start making new memories.'

Milly slipped her hand into Jimmy's and suggested they let the sisters get further ahead, so they could visit their old haunts together and talk some more about the future.

On the return journey on the ferry, Milly extended an invitation to Jimmy's mother and her sister for afternoon tea at her grandmother's on Easter Monday. Jimmy's aunt instantly accepted for them both, saying she was looking forward to meeting Milly's father, having heard so much about the search for him from Anne.

When Milly arrived back at her grandmother's house in Waterloo, she was bubbling over with excitement. It might still be some way off before she and Jimmy would be husband and wife, but it now seemed possible they could stop worrying about his mother's aversion to their marriage.

–

At afternoon tea the following day, Jimmy's mother mentioned to Joseph that she was seriously considering leaving Liverpool and finding herself an apartment in New Brighton.

'That sounds a great idea,' he said encouragingly. 'There'll be lots for you to see and do over there. You're bound to miss Jimmy, but I bet he and Milly will visit you regularly because of where you'll be living.'

'That's what my sister said,' she responded, 'and then there's the grandchildren to look forward to, as well.'

Joseph smilingly agreed, thinking he had never thought about being a grandfather one day himself when he had realised his future lay with Tim. He remembered the day he had sent Bridget and Milly to his mother's in England, knowing he was going to miss his little daughter. Still, life had turned out better than he had hoped; he and Tim could be together and what with him having won money on the races, they could buy their own boat and sail around the world without raising eyebrows when they showed affection for each other. He had done the right thing for Milly, as she would not have made the good friends she had or met Jimmy. His mother would find some happiness in her middle years despite letting her son go, just as he'd let Milly go. He glanced about him and caught Tim's eye and winked, knowing he would never be able to discuss with his daughter the truth about why he had chosen to disappear. Then his gaze fell upon his daughter and Jimmy talking animatedly to Eileen and Barnaby, and Joseph's heart filled with wonder and affection at how his family had been pulled apart by circumstance but were now joined back together again.

Suddenly Milly turned her head and met her father's smiling gaze, thinking how nice-looking he was now he had got rid of his beard. She would miss him and Tim when they went back to sea, but she was so glad that they had come to Liverpool first, and that she was reunited with her daddy and making new memories with him to carry into her future with Jimmy. How different that future would have been if Joseph had not gone missing. She might never have met Anne and Andrew which meant no Jimmy or friends like Kyle and Jane and there

330

would have been no little brother Charlie. Indeed, Kyle and Jane might never have grown close and be getting married. Milly found herself drifting into a daydream, imagining her wedding to Jimmy. She had attended so many weddings during the last two years and she worked out that Kyle and Jane's would be the fourth. She suddenly remembered Barnaby getting Kyle a ticket for the Irish Sweepstake and that a day or so after the Grand National the *Liverpool Echo* reported that several winning tickets had been bought in Liverpool. How wonderful it would be if Kyle's ticket was one of them! But, surely, he wouldn't have kept it a secret from his friends.

–

Milly was not to discover the answer to that question until the day of their wedding on the first Saturday in June when Kyle announced that he did indeed have a winning ticket and that he and Jane had bought a house in Newsham Drive overlooking the park, as well as the house where Jane had been living. They would be moving into Newsham Drive when they returned from their honeymoon and were looking for a tenant for Jane's former home at a rent to be agreed.

Milly wasted no time speaking to Kyle and volunteering to be his first tenant, thinking that having a house ready for her and Jimmy to turn into a home as soon as they were able to wed was the first step on the way to make it happen. She would be close to family and friends whom she could invite round and see her parents whenever they came to Liverpool.

In the meantime, she had been taking typing lessons again with Violet who thought her standard was very high and she would have no trouble getting a job; Andrew had even promised to put a good word in with the *Liverpool Echo*, who were always on the lookout for good typists to take the copy from the field reporters over the phone, then type it up for the next day's newspapers.

Unexpectedly and sadly, Milly's grandmother died shortly after Kyle and Jane's wedding. Despite the sadness, Adelaide had been happier than she had been for a long time in the last couple of months of her life. Addie and her fella came over from Ireland for the funeral and surprisingly so did a pregnant Bridget and her husband. It was not until most of the guests had left after the funeral meal that that the close family gathered in the parlour to listen to Adelaide's will being read out.

There were a few surprises and little actual money. She left her jewellery to her granddaughter Milly and the two nieces, Adelaide and Eileen, stating specifically who was to have what and providing a history of each piece. His father's watch and the car she left to her only son, Joseph, on the condition that Milly's fiancé Jimmy and her nephew Luke could make use of it while Joseph was away at sea. The house and its contents were to be sold and a tenth of the money was to be given to her parish church, a tenth to the holiday home for poor city children, and the remaining money was to be divided between Milly and Joseph and her faithful maid Susan and her husband Leo. She also left a small legacy to Violet.

Milly was pleased that her grandmother had remembered Susan in her will and that she, herself was receiving a sum of money that would come in handy in the light of her having to buy some new furniture and hopefully make some structural alterations to the house. There was also the expense of her wedding to Jimmy the following year when she would be sixteen going on seventeen; she decided to sell one of the rings she had inherited and keep the pearl necklace, the gold and sapphire brooch and the ruby and diamond ring to wear. There was also to be a bigger surprise as just before her father and Tim left to join their ship, Joseph handed her an envelope with a hundred pounds inside and a loving letter in which he wrote that he had earned the money over the years and he'd rather she had it now while he was alive. Milly glowed at the final line which told her that it would come in handy over the next few months but that he'd be back in time to give her away at her wedding. Milly placed the letter back in the envelope and kissed it before placing it next to the photograph of him she kept by her bedside.

She thought to herself, I'll always be a daddy's girl.